THOSE OLDIES

BUT GOODIES

THOSE OLDIES BUT GOODIES

A GUIDE TO 50'S RECORD COLLECTING

STEVE PROPES

COLLIER BOOKS
A Division of Macmillan Publishing Co., Inc.
NEW YORK
COLLIER MACMILLAN PUBLISHERS
LONDON

ACKNOWLEDGMENTS

Thanks to Dick Horlick and Mike Saito for their help.

The author would like to acknowledge the use of various portions of
music publications throughout the work, particularly:
Hill and Range Songs, Inc., for permission to use extracts from
"One Mint Julep" by Rudolph Toombs, Copyright 1952 by
Hill and Range Songs, Inc.; "Crawlin' " by Rudolph Toombs,
Copyright 1953 by Hill and Range Songs, Inc.; "Bip Bam" by
Charles Calhoun, Copyright 1954 by Hill and Range Songs, Inc.;
"Greenbacks" by Renald Richard, Copyright 1954 by Hill and
Range Songs, Inc.; and Dooto Records for "Speedin' " by
Vernon Green, Dootsie Williams publisher.

Macmillan Publishing Co., Inc.
866 Third Avenue, New York, N.Y. 10022
Collier-Macmillan Canada Ltd., Toronto, Ontario

*Those Oldies but Goodies: A Guide to 50's Record
Collecting* is also published in a hardcover edition
by Macmillan Publishing Co., Inc.

Library of Congress Catalog Card Number: 72-93630

Second Printing 1973

Printed in the United States of America

To Sylvia, Heather and Shea

CONTENTS

THOSE OLDIES

BUT GOODIES

INTRODUCTION

This book is dedicated to the collector and to that turn of thought that motivates and nurtures the pursuit of seeking out, acquiring and assembling individual works into a creative whole: a collection.

Those Oldies but Goodies is the first systematic attempt to describe and define those elements that constitute a valid collection of 1950's music. I could not include all recorded works from that era, but I do touch on what I feel are the most significant and influential records.

Here are the ground rules of what records to look for, where to look, prices to pay (especially for rare records) and pitfalls to avoid. Further, discographies of the significant vocal groups and single artists dominating rhythm and blues and rock and roll during the 1950's are provided. Because of the formative nature of these artists' records, the period 1950 to 1959 can truly be called the Classic Era of rock and roll. By giving as full and accurate discographical information as available, the releases of various artists are put into historic and artistic perspective.

I wish to direct this body of data not only to the established collector, but also, and especially, to the person with enough interest in early rock and roll and rhythm and blues originals to assemble a personal collection of this important art form.

RARE RECORDS

Collecting has become a refined art when applied to paintings, furniture, stamps, coins and antique items. Books, guides and systems of value have been created that are widely accepted by the buyer, seller and dealer. Clubs, auction houses and retail outlets have been successful in the collector's item trade. In short, these forms of collecting are acceptable, respectable and maybe a little dull.

That's surely not the case with 1950's record collecting. Values are far from firm, markets have not been cornered and reliable dealerships are few and far between. Thus there is no universal acceptance and respectability attached to this collecting form.

Recordings of the 1950's are usually sold cheaply or discarded by the noncollector and snubbed by collectors of other types of sound recordings. To the collector specializing in opera or the classics, prewar jazz, blues, gospel, early hillbilly or big band records, the 1950's 78 or 45 RPM recording is just too new to be taken seriously as a collector's item. Nevertheless, 1950's music is becoming recognized as an honest and unique art form quite worthy of assuming a collectable status. Consequently, systems of value are being developed.

One of the reasons for the comparative rarity of certain records was the reluctance of major and minor record companies to press more than a few thousand copies of rhythm and blues and rock and roll releases. In comparison with today's practice of abundant overpressings, the number of copies of the typical 1950's release is insignificant. During the 50's sales of a few thousand records constituted a fair-sized hit. Only when the heavy sales potential was obvious, as with big smashes like Patti Page's "Old Cape Cod" or Pat Boone's "Love Letters in the Sand," were records pressed in large numbers. Today even a fair-sized flop is usually overpressed.

During the 50's, if by some remote chance a record store or distributor got stuck with unsold records, they usually returned them to the pressing plant for recycling. It was uncommon for any unsold records to avoid the melting process. Today this practice is rare among record dealers and distributors. If a record doesn't sell at ninety-eight cents, it will sell at fifty-nine cents, three for a buck or in ten for a dollar packs. In short, 60's releases are much easier to obtain than 50's releases.

There is another inescapable fact of a record collector's life—record companies are deletion crazy. They've deleted 78's altogether, and they constantly purge from their catalogs more long-playing albums and 45's than they release. Also they delete themselves. Hundreds of record companies have folded after a few releases. Of course, the Beatles, Creedence Clearwater and Elvis are not deleted, because they maintain continuing popularity. But for every Beatles issue, Capitol has discontinued hundreds of great releases by such artists as T-Bone Walker, the Five Keys and Johnny Otis—records of varying commercial success but almost always of great value in an artistic sense and as a statement of the era.

Among collectors values are far from universally known. In fact, for the most part, they are based on what a given collector will pay for a record and thus are not firmly set. The value of a particular record, then, depends principally upon comparative rarity and desirability. Some records are so obscure that, although they are very rare and very good, the fact that the average collector does not know of them makes them of lesser value. Again, value depends largely upon demand.

Some records are more attractive to collectors. The more that the rarity of a given record is discussed and rumored, the greater its value becomes. Some highly attractive rare records take on a charismatic value. Three such discs are the Flamingos' "I Really Don't Want to Know," the Five Keys' "Red Sails in the Sunset" and the legendary "Stormy Weather" by the Five Sharps.

Long-time rhythm and blues collectors tend to attach the greatest value to the slow, sweetly romantic ballad—the so-called Do-Wop vocal group record—preferably released in the very early 50's. "Stormy Weather" possesses more than the usual desirability because the sound of the original recording is only remembered. No one seems to own a copy or a tape of it, and the master was lost in a fire. Not even Jubilee records owns a copy. Thus "Stormy Weather" by the Five Sharps is the premium item for most vocal group collectors—a one-of-a-kind original would be the prize of any collection. Because of the great demand, in 1965 Jubilee number 5478 entitled "Stormy Weather" by the Five Sharps was recorded and released. It is a poor rock and roll version by a totally different group. The search for the original continues.

The going prices for rare and not so rare 45 RPM records can be established on a rule-of-thumb basis. However, these prices are subject to frequent variance.

	By Vocal Groups	By Single Blues and Rockabilly Artists
Rarest records	$35 and up (occasionally from $50 to $100 plus)	$15 and up
Rare records	$15 to $35	$5 to $10
Fairly rare records	$5 to $15	$2 to $5
Common or fairly common records	$2 to $5	$1 to $2

The highest prices apply to the mint or near-mint original. Obviously, the collector who will settle for only the original in mint condition must be prepared to pay handsomely for his preference.

Grading the Condition of Records

There exists a common rating system useful for the grading of new and used records. This system was introduced by the

Record Changer magazine in the late 40's and was adopted by collectors and dealers for use in auction and sale lists. The current crop of collector's magazines have also adopted the system. Mint (M) condition indicates a record with no visual or audible scratches or defects on the wax or label. It is a fresh, unplayed record and thus commands the highest price. Some collectors insist on records in mint condition only.

Very Good (VG) condition indicates the record has a minimum of foreign noises, wear and scratches. This record has been played, but has been handled with care and stored properly in a sleeve. Most collectors are quite satisfied with records in very good condition, though their value is usually less than that of a mint record.

Good (G) condition is used for a record that has been played often, thus producing a moderate amount of noise. There are scratches and obvious foreign sounds; however, the music is clearly more prominent than the interference. In most cases, this record is kept in collections only until a copy in VG or better condition can be located.

Fair (F) condition means the music and the distortion are equal. Listening requires some effort. This record is worn.

Poor (P) condition indicates the distortion is more prominent than the music, producing little satisfaction in listening. Since such a record can damage a stylus, it is only suitable for experimenting in warp correction or as a wall hanging.

Pluses and minuses are used to refine these ratings. Thus a record in VG— condition is in somewhat better shape than one in G+ condition. However, these distinctions can become hazy. Grading, after all, is subjective, depending on the grader's ear, his equipment and other variables, and thus can be a source of controversy and misunderstanding.

RECORD LABELS

Most record companies, major and minor, adapted to the 45 RPM speed in the early 50's. RCA developed the 45 RPM disc in 1949 and most of the majors followed suit soon after. The smaller rhythm and blues companies, losing jukebox trade to the majors, soon conformed, although several did not change until 1954. Quite often the record company retroactively converted their earlier 78 RPM releases to 45 RPM at the time of the changeover. Most companies phased out the 78 RPM speed in 1958, again with RCA taking the lead.

A chronological breakdown follows, showing the founding date of each company along with the year it first issued recordings on 45 RPM.

The Majors:

Label	Date Founded	Date 45 RPM Introduced	Label	Date Founded	Date 45 RPM Introduced
Columbia	1885	1949	Mercury	1946	1950
RCA Victor	1901	1949	Coral	1949	1949
Decca	1934	1949	Brunswick	1956	1956
Capitol	1942	1949	ABC	1956	1956
MGM	1946	1950			

The Smaller Rhythm and Blues Labels (by region):

East Coast Labels	Date Founded	Date 45 RPM Introduced	West Coast Labels	Date Founded	Date 45 RPM Introduced
Savoy	1943	1950	Aladdin	1945	1951
Manor	1945	(—)	Modern	1945	1950
Jubilee	1948	1950	Swingtime	1946	1951
Deluxe	1948	1951	Specialty	1946	1951
Atlantic	1948	1951	Imperial	1947	1951
Gotham	1949	1952	RPM	1950	1950
Okeh	1951	1951	Hollywood	1950	1950
Herald	1952	1952	Dootone	1950	1954
Rama	1953	1953	Flair	1953	1953
Bruce	1953	1953	Crown	1953	1953
Red Robin	1953	1953	Spark	1954	1954
Groove	1954	1954	Money	1954	1954
Josie	1954	1954	Cash	1954	1954
Gee	1955	1955	R & B	1954	1954
Atco	1955	1955	Flip	1955	1955
Baton	1955	1955	Dig	1955	1955
Melba	1955	1955	Liberty	1955	1955

Midwest Labels	Date Founded	Date 45 RPM Introduced	Southern Labels	Date Founded	Date 45 RPM Introduced
King	1945	1951	Peacock	1949	1951
Chess	1949	1951	Duke	1952	1952
Chance	1950	1950	Sun	1953	1953
Federal	1950	1950	Excello	1953	1953
Checker	1952	1952	Ace	1955	1955
Vee Jay	1953	1953			
Parrot	1953	1953			
Fortune	1954	1954			

Of the East Coast labels, New York was the headquarters for all but the Gotham label of Philadelphia, and Savoy, DeLuxe and Jubilee, which were established in New Jersey. All of the

West Coast labels listed were headquartered in Los Angeles. The San Francisco Bay Area was headquarters for the Music City and Rhythm labels. Chicago was home base for Chess-Checker, Chance, Parrot and Vee Jay; Federal and King were headquartered in Cincinnati; while the home base for Fortune was Detroit. Peacock and Duke were in Houston; Sun was a famous Memphis label; Excello was based in Nashville and Ace in Jackson, Mississippi.

Most collectors prefer the 45 RPM issue—the 78 is bulkier and usually not as rare, the LP is almost always just a reissue. The 78 RPM record of unusual value is the one that was never released on 45 RPM or is scarcer than the 45 RPM issue. The 78 RPM record released in the very late 50's at the point in time when the speed was rendered extinct by the 45 is usually much rarer than the 45 RPM version. One of the rarest 78's is "Fannie Mae" by Buster Brown, released in 1959. Any 78 RPM record from this year or later is probably rarer than the 45 RPM issue.

Some of the rarest 45 RPM records are those released in 1950 or earlier. Some of the earliest Orioles recordings exist on 45 RPM even though they were originally pressed on 78 RPM and reissued on 45. It is in such an example that the reissue (the 45 RPM record) is now more valuable than the original issue.

Most record labels reissued successful recordings in various ways. The subject of reissues is extremely complex but several examples are enlightening.

Many smaller record companies had their records produced by various pressing plants throughout the country. These pressing companies would often redesign the label, change the colors of the label or the size or type of the print, or otherwise alter its appearance. Such changes make identifying a record in terms of its vintage or chronology a subject of continuing controversy. Also the smaller companies would sell or lease certain artists or recordings to larger firms, which would re-release the material. It's often confusing to trace these releases. The comparative rarity of these recordings is also difficult to establish. Infrequently the re-release is rarer than the more successful original. Reportedly the Decca reissue of the Hollywood Flames' material originally on Lucky is now rarer than the original—but is it more valuable? The subject is indeed controversial.

The Dootone label released early 45 RPM records on a red label. A hit such as the incredible "Earth Angel" by the Penguins caused such a demand that the pressing plants soon ran out of the red paper and went to maroon, blue and black paper simultaneously. Thus early Dootone releases on labels of different colors are all originals; however, the red label is usually considered the premium original. Later the Dootone label became Dooto and adopted a complex multicolor design to make bootlegging difficult.

Other companies were much more consistent with label colors. Early Atlantic Records 45 RPM issues were yellow and black to distinguish from the red and black 78 RPM releases. With the issuance of Atlantic 1083, the yellow label was discontinued on 45 RPM and all future issues were on the red and black label. Thus any early (pre-Atlantic 1083) 45 RPM releases on the red and black label are reissues and of less value than the yellow and black originals.

The style of print or the size or shape of the label design can also identify an original. The original Imperial label was blue with silver print and "Imperial" was in a fancy script design. With the approximate release number of 5299 the label color was changed to red but the script design remained the same. With issue number 5357 the script print was dropped in favor of block print on a blue label. Thus an original pre-5357 Imperial 45 RPM record must have the script printing. The difference is subtle but the bearing it has on value is often substantial.

Design characteristics of other major rhythm and blues labels are all-important in separating the original from the reissue (in several cases the issue numbers consistent with the changing designs can only be estimated).

Reissues of very old rhythm and blues hits have been pressed for years and in many cases continue to sell very well. These reissues are legally authorized reproductions released either by the original record company with different label designs and often with different flip sides (an unfortunate trend as the original flip side is often as good, if not better, than the "A" side), or by reissue labels specializing in rhythm and blues material. The latter include Lost Nite, Times Square and the now defunct Oldies 45 (notorious for the poor quality of the wax). Too frequently the major record companies have altered the sound of the original work to make it "up to date." Generally,

Label	Issue Number	Color and Label Design
Aladdin	3000 to approx. 3259	Blue with silver print
	3260 to approx. 3400	Maroon with silver print
	3400 to 3460	Black with silver print
Argo	5250 to approx. 5280	Black with silver top
	5280 to approx. 5400	Black with silver print "Argo" vertically placed
Atco	6050 to 6090	Maroon with yellow print
	6090 to present	Yellow and white label
Checker	750 to 875	Maroon with silver print Checkerboard design on top
	875 to 1100	Maroon with silver print "Checker" vertically placed
Chess	1450 to 1670	Blue with silver top
	1670 to 1800	Blue with silver print "Chess" vertically placed
Federal	12000 to 12160	Green with gold top
	12160 to 12200	Green with silver top
	12200 to present	All green label
King	4100 to 4900	Blue with silver print
		Reissues of this series have "high fidelity" on label, originals do not
Modern	600 to 900	Shiny black label with silver print
	900 to 980	Shiny blue or red label with silver print
	980 to 1025	Dull black label
Peacock	1500 to 1680	Red label with silver print
	1680 to present	White label with black print
Rama	1 to approx. 200	Blue label with silver print
	200 to end of series	Red label with silver print

Label	Issue Number	Color and Label Design
RPM	300 to 360	Black label with silver print "RPM" in large letters
	360 to 460	Red or blue label with silver print "RPM" in smaller letters
	460 to 500	Dull black label
Specialty	300 to 604	Yellow and white with double wavy lines
	604 to present	Yellow and white with solid line
Vee Jay	100 to 350	Maroon with silver print
	350 to end of series	Black with silver print

this practice dilutes and interferes with the recorded perform-ance and makes it into something it was never intended to be. The addition of extra instrumentation to the beautiful harmony of the Penguins' "Earth Angel," or narration, strings and a chorus to Jerry Butler's "For Your Precious Love," for example, neither improves the record nor indicates the artists' original intentions.

Bootlegs are relatively inexpensive, identical (more or less) reproductions of the original label and recorded performance. As with the illegal reproduction of current rock LP's and tapes, bootlegs of rare oldies are improving in quality, as their popu-larity grows. The cost of bootlegs has recently been reduced from the $5 to $10 range to the more reasonable neighborhood of $2 or $3 per copy.

There are obvious dangers inherent in the bootleg. If you are offered a 45 RPM copy of a very rare record in mint condi-tion at a bargain price—be careful. Chances are it's a "boot" being offered as an original.

However, at reasonable prices, bootlegs are a good way of collecting an otherwise almost unobtainable recording. Some of the records most commonly bootlegged include:

Aladdin 3031	"Don't Like the Way You're Doing" by the Robins
Aladdin 3127	"Red Sails in the Sunset" by the Five Keys
Chariot 103	"Doll Face" by the Vibranaires

Chance 1150	"Just a Lonely Christmas" by the Moonglows
Columbia 39408	"You Foolish Thing" by the Ravens
Federal 12077	"Starting from Tonight" by the Royals
Gee 10	"Can't Get No Place with You" by the Coins
Hollywood 1059	"Dear Heart" by Jesse Belvin
Kicks 1	"A Dream Come True" by the Squires
Parrot 808	"Dream of a Lifetime" by the Flamingos
Rainbow 122	"Yes Sir That's My Baby" by the Clovers
Sabre 108	"The Beat of Our Hearts" by the Five Blue Notes
Vee Jay 134	"Tell the World" by the Dells

Bootlegging, of course, is illegal, and apparently the producers and dealers in rare 50's music have been feeling the same heat as rock bootleggers. Thus the availability of the boot is subject to change without notice.

Many record companies issued the bulk of their releases on solid black wax with a few on transparent colored wax. For the most part, a record on colored wax is much more valuable than the more widely distributed black vinyl version. The most usual vinyl colors are red and blue, then green; orange, yellow and other colors are very unusual. The companies most frequently associated with colored vinyl records are RCA, King, Federal, Chance, Vee Jay, De Luxe and Rama. Imperial and Specialty used a solid nontransparent colored wax.

These are a few of the varying physical characteristics that affect the value of records. The beginning collector should consider them, but should also keep in mind that a good record sounds just as good on a reissue label or on black vinyl.

THE RECORDED SOUND

Early 50's rhythm and blues recordings often dealt with subject matter of great and personal importance to their audience. They treated both pleasant and unpleasant themes in an honest and compelling manner, often boastfully proclaiming the joys of living.

The positive or pleasant themes included:

1. Sex and virility
2. Partying and night life
3. Fast cars

The negative or problem themes included:

1. Drinking (occasionally presented in a boastful manner)
2. Money problems
3. Crime, punishment and dangerous situations
4. Remorse and appeals for religious help

Another subject found in later rhythm and blues records was adolescent problems. "Yakety Yak" by the Coasters is an example of the theme, which was a derivative of white rock and roll. However, the earlier themes were all original to rhythm and blues.

SEX AND VIRILITY

"Sixty Minute Man" by the Dominoes expresses virility, as the lead singer boldly identifies himself as "lovin' Dan." The sexual meaning of the claim "There'll be fifteen minutes of blowin' my top" is apparent.

"Laundromat Blues" by the Five Royales is blatantly and almost crudely sexual. The singer uses such phrases as "Her machine is full of suds" and "It will cost you 30¢ a pound" to analogize his girl's sexual habits to a washing machine. One of the best records with sexual lyrics was the Swallows' release "It Ain't the Meat"—"it's the motion." It is literally loaded with sexual references such as "It's the movement that gives it the sock" and "She wraps all around me like a rubber band."

Another early release was the Royals' (Midnighters) very successful "Work with Me Annie." This may be the best-known sexual record as it generated a whole series of "Annie" records by the Midnighters and other groups.

"Toy Bell" by the Bees is an extremely funny and effective double entendre—"When I play with my ding-a-ling."

"Big Ten Inch Record" by Bullmoose Jackson is not at all subtle in the refrain: "She just loves my big ten inch . . . (pause) . . . record of her favorite blues."

Other well-known records with sexual lyrics include the Drifters' "Bip Bam" ("thank'ya m'am"), "Ride Helen Ride" (the word "ride" was used often in an erotic sense) by the Hollywood Flames and "Let Me Bang Your Box" by the Toppers.

In "I'm a Man" by Bo Diddley, the singer testifies to his prowess and says he can make love to his baby in an hour.

Other records with implications of virility are "Brown-Eyed Handsome Man" by Chuck Berry and "Hootchie Coochie Man" by Muddy Waters.

DRINKING

"One Mint Julep" by the Clovers is a two-minute-twenty-second morality play tracing a man's downfall from drinking, to a shotgun wedding, to having "six extra children from a-gettin' frisky." The moral: "One mint julep was the cause of it all." "Crawlin'," also by the Clovers, reflects on drinking in the refrain, "I'll be crawlin' instead of ballin'." "Nip Sip" by the Clovers is a more positive view of alcohol: "Got a dollar for my nippin' and a dime for my lunch." The Five Keys also advocate regular drinking—"Gonna wake up sober, start all over"—in their "Serve Another Round." "WPLJ," by the Four Deuces, is a singing mixed-drink recipe for "white port lemon juice."

"Let Me Go Home Whiskey" by Amos Milburn is an alcoholic's story—"As long as I get my whiskey everything's all right."

"I Got Loaded" by Peppermint Harris describes a classic barroom drinking session: "I took a sip every trip that bottle passed around."

Other records primarily concerned with drinking were Amos Milburn's "One Scotch, One Bourbon, One Beer," "Empty Bottles" by the Robins and "Drinkin' Wine Spo Dee O Dee," originally by Sticks McGhee and later by Wynonie Harris and the Johnny Burnette Trio.

PARTYING AND NIGHT LIFE

Amos Milburn's "Chicken Shack Boogie" is a party in itself, a fantastic boogie piano workout about a place "where you get a whole lot of good things to eat." Milburn's "House Party" has "room for more, keep comin' in the door."

Let the Good Times Roll by Shirley and Lee is another good-time record with an exciting rollicking tempo. It's one of the all-time classics from the 50's.

Other party records include "Rip It Up" by Little Richard, "Mardi Gras in New Orleans" by Fats Domino, Chuck Berry's "Roll Over Beethoven," "Johnny's House Party" by Johnny Heartsman on the Music City label and "Saturday Nite Fish Fry" by Louis Jordan on Decca.

FAST CARS

The Medallions had several amazing releases on the subject of speeding cars, especially "Speedin'" and "Buick '59." These songs consisted of up-tempo harmony, the singers using their voices to imitate powerful motors, squealing tires, police sirens, and in *Speedin'*, a flat tire: "bloop bloop bloop bloop . . . oh oh I done had a flat. Never mind that buddy, where's your license?"

"Speedo" by the Cadillacs is simply the lead singer comparing his abilities to a fast car.

"Maybellene" by Chuck Berry is a car chase in pursuit of his girl, Maybellene, who is in a "coupe de ville," while Berry is in a "V-8 Ford."

Other songs about cars were Todd Rhodes' "Rocket 69" and "Rocket 88" by Jackie Brenston and later by Bill Haley.

CRIME, PUNISHMENT AND DANGEROUS SITUATIONS

The Robins made several records about trouble with the law and prison life. "Riot in Cell Block #9," with Richard Berry as the lead singer, and Berry's follow-up, "The Big Break," are essentially the same performance—a dramatic narrative of a prison riot from the prisoner's point of view. "Framed" was a much less grim first-person account by a man wrongly arrested, charged and convicted, "But when the judge came down, poured whiskey on my head, turned around to the jury and said 'Convict this man he is drunk,' what could I do?" In "Smokey Joe's Café," the third record by the group, the main character is menaced with a knife by Smokey Joe, who warns ominously, "You better eat up all your beans, boy, and clear right on out."

"Thirty Days" by Chuck Berry is a warning to his girl that he has a sheriff's warrant to bring her home in thirty days or they would bring charges against her.

"Stagger Lee" by Lloyd Price is a blow-by-blow description of a dice game. Apparently two versions of this record were released. The first contained a tragic aftermath—Stagger Lee shoots his opponent, Billy: "He shot that poor boy so bad, till the bullet came through Billy and it broke the bartender's glass." The second, a much milder version with no hint of violence or death, is the only one now available.

"The Bells" by the Dominoes features a strong Clyde Mc-Phatter lead, complete with sobbing gasps and occasional shrieks, particularly at the finish. The song is about his girl's funeral ("roses all around my baby's head") and his begging her forgiveness. This morbidity is a forerunner of Donald Woods' "Death of an Angel." There is great similarity between the two songs. "Death of an Angel" was banned by some radio stations because of its overwhelming effect on the listener. Some teenage girls were driven to emulate the heroine—by attempting suicide.

"Deep Sea Blues" by the Dominoes begins with a single piano note—"The deep sea is calling me." A somber mood is effectively set. Again, Clyde McPhatter captures the dramatic essence of suicidal depression: "I'll be waiting for you in the deep blue sea." The 1958 hit, Jody Reynolds' "Endless Sleep," bears resemblance to this Dominoes record.

"Crying in the Chapel" by the Orioles is a milder expression of remorse and even eventually expresses joy, with Sonny Till resolving that "I am happy with the Lord."

A statement of bitterness is the spoken recitation in the Velvetones' "Glory of Love": "You feel you're too good, much too good, for a nobody like me." Though it is a cornball declaration of jilted love, it was a successful record.

Recordings about money usually dealt with the subject either from the viewpoint of the cheated or the broke and busted, the down and out.

In "Greenbacks" by Ray Charles, the lesson is about a girl he meets, telling him to "Let Lincoln and Jackson start shaking hands." She finally splits with his cash, "Just a little piece of paper coated with chlorophyl."

"Money Honey" by Clyde McPhatter and the Drifters repeats

a basic theme: "You've gotta have money, honey, if you wanta' get along with me."

"Your Cash Ain't Nothing but Trash" by the Clovers expresses an opposite sentiment. The singer's efforts at impressing girls and businessmen with money get him nowhere.

RHYTHM AND BLUES GROUPS

Rhythm and blues vocal groups recorded in several distinct styles:

1. Early (pre-1950) recordings by the Ravens and the Four Tunes, among others, were in a nearly pop or "white"-sounding style—not really down-to-earth rhythm and blues.

2. The rhythm and blues style is much more evident in the early ballad efforts of the Orioles, the Dominoes, the Five Keys and the Swallows, recorded in the very early '50's. The sound was mellow and sweet, not at all pop, totally in the rhythm and blues tradition.

3. Uptempo or jump recordings by these and other early vocal groups such as the Robins and the Drifters were heavily influenced by blues. The rhythms were primitive and the vocals were quite straightforward.

4. "Gee" by the Crows, a sophisticated big city jump sound released in 1953, was the predecessor of the later, very successful rock and roll style.

5. In 1955–1956, the rock and roll style achieved success and became the dominant uptempo format.

6. With the success of rock and roll, the ballad became more sophisticated, adopting a strong beat at the expense of the earlier more mellow sound.

The following rhythm and blues vocal groups were the most significant during the 50's. The sound was innovated by the Ravens and several other groups during the late 40's. Later vocal groups developed distinct regional sounds and approaches to their music: the New York–Philadelphia "East Coast Sound" was relatively sophisticated "street corner harmony"; the Los Angeles "West Coast Sound" had definite blues and jazz influences; and the Chicago–Detroit–Cincinnati "Midwest Sound," stemming somewhat from Chicago blues, often contained off-color lyrics.

In the following chronological and regional breakdown of the most important vocal groups the regional criteria are largely based on the home location of the record company, and thus the sound the group adopted.

Rhythm and Blues Vocal Groups:

Year	East Coast	Midwest	West Coast
1946	The Ravens		
1947	The Four Tunes		
1948	The Orioles		
1949			The Robins
1950	The Clovers	The Dominoes	The Hollywood Flames
1951	The Cardinals	The Swallows	The Five Keys Jesse Belvin
1952	The Five Royales	The Royals (The Midnighters) The Checkers The Moonglows	
1953	The Drifters The Charms The Crows The Harptones	The Flamingos The Platters The Spaniels The El Rays (The Dells)	The Flairs
1954	The Cadillacs	The El Dorados	The Jewels The Spiders The Meadowlarks The Penguins The Medallions
1955	The Heartbeats The Five Satins		Arthur Lee Maye & the Crowns The Cadets (The Jacks)

These are the landmark rhythm and blues vocal groups of the era. A brief examination of the history and sound of each group, the current rarity and value of their records and a complete discography follow.

The Ravens

HISTORY AND SOUND

One of the handful of vocal groups (along with the Ink Spots, the Delta Rhythm Boys and the Four Tunes) that pioneered the rhythm and blues sound and style, the Ravens' first recordings were for the fledgling King Record Company in 1946. The Ravens maintained consistent popularity throughout the late 40's and into the mid-50's. Most of their recordings featured the deep voice of lead singer Jimmy Ricks. Ricks can be heard in the rocking "Wagon Wheels" and in the beautiful ballad "Count Every Star" (a 1958 best-seller for the Rivieras). The Ravens' recording of "White Christmas" was the original rhythm and blues version from which the Drifters drew their consistently selling smash hit. In the mid and late 50's, the quality of the Ravens' recordings declined. The group stopped recording around 1958.

RARITY AND VALUE

The earliest recordings on King, Hub and National were not all released on 45 RPM, but those that were are now extremely rare. The King and Hub 78's are now much rarer than the better-selling National recordings. The Columbia and Okeh releases (Columbia 39408 and Okeh 6825 in particular) are now among the rarest 45's. The Mercury records are fairly rare (in the $8 to $12 range) with several, including "September Song," bringing up to $35 in record auctions. The Jubilee and

Argo recordings reflect the decline of the group and are generally worth from $5 to $10.

DISCOGRAPHY

King

4234	"Bye Bye Baby Blues"/"Song of India"	1946
4260	"Out of a Dream"/"Blues in the Clouds"	
4272	"Honey"/"Matinee Here in New Orleans"	
4293	"My Sugar Is So Refined"/"Playing Around"	

Hub

3030	"Honey"/"Lullaby"	1946
3032	"My Sugar Is So Refined"/"Out of a Dream"	
3033	"Bye Bye Baby Blues"/"Once and for All"	

National

9034	"For You"/"Mahel"	1947
9035	"Ol' Man River"/"Would You Believe Me"	
9038	"Write Me a Letter"/"Summertime"	
9039	"Searching for Love"/"For You"	
9040	"Fool That I Am"/"Bee I Bumble Bee or Not"	
9042	"Together"/"There's No You"	1948
9045	"Send for Me if You Need Me"/"Until the Real Thing Comes Along"	
9053	"September Song"/"Once in Awhile"	
9056	"It's Too Soon to Know"/"Be on Your Merry Way"	
9059	"How Could I Know"/"Don't Know Why"	
9062	"White Christmas"/"Silent Night"	
9064	"Always"/"Rooster"	1949
9065	"Deep Purple"/"Leave My Gal Alone"	
9073	"Ricky's Blues"/"The House I Live in"	
9085	"There's Nothing Like a Woman in Love"/"Careless Love"	
9089	"Someday"/"If You Didn't Mean It"	
9098	"Get Wise Baby"/"I'm Afraid of You"	

9101   "Don't Have to Ride No More"/"I've Been a Fool"
9111   "Count Every Star"/"I'm Gonna Paper My Walls
        with Your Letters"   1950
9131   "Phantom Stage Coach"/"I'm Gonna Take to the
        Road"
9148   "Lilacs in the Rain"/"Time Is Marching on"
Rendition
5001   "Marie"/"Write Me a Letter"
Columbia
39050   "Time Takes Care of Everything"/"Don't
        Look Now"   1950
39070   "I'm So Crazy for Love"/"My Baby's Gone"
39112   "Midnite Blues"/"Don't Drop a Heart to Break It"
39194   "You're Always in My Dreams"/"Gotta Find
        My Baby"   1951
39408   "You Foolish Thing"/"Honey, I Don't Want You"
Okeh
6825   "The Whiffenpoof Song"/"I Get My Lovin'
        on a Saturday Night"   1951
6843   "Everything But You"/"That Old Gang"
6888   "Mamselle"/"Calypso Song"
6912   "Someone to Watch over Me"/"The Shy One"
6928   "Lil' Sonny"/"Linger Awhile"
Mercury
5764   "Wagon Wheels"/"There's No Use
        Pretending"   1952
5800   "Looking for My Baby"/"Begin the Beguine"
5853   "Chloe-E"/"Why Did You Leave Me"
8257   "Out in the Cold Again"/"Hey Good Looking"
        (with Dinah Washington)
8291   "Rock Me All Night Long"/"Write Me One
        Sweet Letter"
70060   "I'll Be Back"/"Don't Mention My Name"   1953
70119   "Come a Little Bit Closer"/"She's Got to Go"
70213   "Rough Ridin' "/"Who'll Be the Fool"

70240	"Without a Song"/"Walkin' My Blues Away"	
70307	"September Song"/"Escortin' or Courtin' "	
70330	"Going Home"/"Lonesome Road"	
70413	"Love Is No Dream"/"I've Got You Under My Skin"	1954
70505	"White Christmas"/"Silent Night"	
70554	"Ol' Man River"/"Write Me a Letter"	

Jubilee
5184	"Bye Bye Baby Blues"/"Happy Go Lucky Baby"	1955
5203	"Green Eyes"/"The Bells of San Raquel"	
5217	"On Chapel Hill"/"We'll Raise a Ruckus Tonight"	
5237	"I'll Always Be in Love with You"/"Boots and Saddles"	1956

Argo
5255	"Kneel and Pray"/"I Can't Believe"	
5261	"A Simple Prayer"/"Water Boy"	1957
5276	"Dear One"/"That'll Be the Day" (also on Checker 871)	
5284	"Here Is My Heart"/"Lazy Mule"	

Savoy
| 1540 | "White Christmas"/"Silent Night" | |

The Four Tunes

HISTORY AND SOUND

The Four Tunes were an early rhythm and blues vocal group with a distinct pop flavor. They began recording in 1947, scoring mild successes on four labels. Several of their first releases were love ballads sung with Savannah Churchill. The group's up-tempo style, so successful on "Marie," is apparent in the earlier "Cool Water." However, for the most part, the Four Tunes specialized in ballads such as "Time Out for Tears" and "Do I Worry." Their first Jubilee record, "Marie," was a phenomenally consistent best-seller in the early 50's. They repeated the success with the ballad "I Understand." As with the Ravens, the Four Tunes suffered a decline in quality with their last releases.

RARITY AND VALUE

If any of the Manor or Columbia releases were pressed on 45 RPM, they are now very rare. "Time Out for Tears" was reputed to have been available on 45 RPM, and if so, would now be extremely rare. The RCA releases are fairly rare, in the $10 to $20 range. The Jubilee releases were good-sellers and generally bring less than $5.

DISCOGRAPHY

Manor
1046	"I Want to Be Loved"/"Foolishly Yours" (with Savannah Churchill)	1947
1047	"I'll Close My Eyes"/"Save Me a Dream"	
1049	"I'd Rather Be Safe than Sorry"/"I'll Be Waiting for You"	
1050	"Too Many Times"/"I'll Always Say I Love You"	
1076	"Darling, You Make It So"/(reverse by Betty Norton)	1947
1077	"Where Is My Love"/"Sometime, Someplace, Somewhere"	
1085	"Wrapped Up in a Dream"/"I Found Love When I Found You"	
1087	"Dreams"/"Chillicothe Ohio" (with Betty Harris)	
1093	"I Understand"/"Is It Too Late" (with Savannah Churchill)	

1116	"Time Out for Tears"/"All My Dreams" (with Savannah Churchill)	
1123	"Little Jane"/"Tell Me So" (with Savannah Churchill)	1948
1129	"Someday"/"I Want to Cry"	
1131	"Confess"/"Don't Know"	
1141	"Don't You Ever Mind"/"How Can I Make You Believe in Me"	
1142	"I'll Never Belong to Anyone Else"/"Try to Forget" (with Savannah Churchill)	
1154	"I'm Gonna Ride Tillie Tonight"/"My Muchacha"	
1168	"Would You Hurt Me Now"/"All of Me" (with Savannah Churchill)	
1173	"Mister Sun"/"The Sheik of Araby"	
1195	"Someday"/"Karen Lynn"	

Arco

1220	"I Want to Cry"/"My Baby-kin" (with Savannah Churchill)	1949
1246	"You're My Love"/"Don't Blame My Dreams"	

Columbia

30145	"Where Is My Love"/"Take My Lonely Heart"	
30146	"The Best of Friends"/"The Things You Do to Me"	

RCA

0016	"I'm the Guy"/"My Last Affair"	
0024	"You're Heartless"/"Careless Love"	
0042	"I'm Just a Fool in Love"/"Lonesome Road" (also on RCA 0058)	
0072	"There Goes My Heart"	
0085	"Kentucky Babe"/"Old-Fashioned Love"	
0131	"May That Day Never Come"/"Carry Me Back to the Lone Prairie"	
3881	"Do I Worry"/"Say When"	1950
3967	"Cool Water"/"How Can You Say That I Don't Care"	
4102	"Wishing You Were Here Tonight"/"The Last Roundup"	1951

4241	"I Married an Angel"/"The Prisoner's Song"	
4305	"Early in the Morning"/"My Buddy"	
4427	"I'll See You in My Dreams"/"Tell Me Why"	
4489	"Come What May"/"The Greatest Song I Ever Heard"	
4663	"I Wonder"/"Can I Say Anymore"	1952
4828	"They Don't Understand"/"Why Do You Do This to Me"	
4968	"Let's Give Love Another Chance"/"I Don't Want to Set the World on Fire"	
5532	"Don't Get Around Much Anymore"/"Water Boy"	1953

Jubilee

5128	"Marie"/"I Gambled with Love"	1953
5132	"I Understand"/"Sugar Lump"	1954
5135	"My Wild Irish Rose"/"Do Do Do Do Do Do Do It Again"	
5152	"Lonesome"/"The Greatest Feeling in the World"	
5165	"Don't Cry Darling"/"L'Amour, Toujours L'Amour"	
5174	"Let Me Go Lover"/"I Sold My Heart to the Junkman"	
5183	"I Hope"/"I Close My Eyes"	1955
5200	"Tired of Waiting"/"Time Out for Tears"	
5212	"Brooklyn Bridge"/"Three Little Chickens"	
5218	"You Are My Love"/"At the Steamboat River Ball"	
5232	"Our Love"/"Rock and Roll Call"	1956
5239	"I Gotta Go"/"Hold Me Closer"	
5245	"Faraway Places"/"Dancing with Tears in My Eyes"	
5255	"Japanese Farewell Song"/"The Ballad of James Dean"	
5276	"A Little on the Lonely Side"/"Cool Water"	
5329	"Hold Me Closer"	

The Orioles

HISTORY AND SOUND

The Orioles were the first pure rhythm and blues group. None of the pop overtones found in the Ravens' or the Four Tunes' recordings is apparent in the Orioles' records. Sonny Til's emotionally charged lead vocals gave great meaning and honesty to all of his recorded performances. The group was simply sensational. Their records sold consistently throughout the early and mid-50's with little apparent loss of luster. The Orioles were responsible for a long string of excellent releases, all now highly prized by collectors. From "It's Too Soon to Know" to "Runaround," this was one of the best set of consecutive performances released by any 50's group.

RARITY AND VALUE

The pre-1950 releases (to approximately Jubilee 5018) are very rare on the original "script" Jubilee 45 RPM label. On colored vinyl, the value of these records is even greater. From 1950 to 1953, and "I Cover the Waterfront," the recordings are rare and sought after by collectors. The earliest releases are worth in excess of $50; the post-1952 recordings often bring prices of $25 to $30. The group had two very large hits in "Crying in the Chapel" and "In the Chapel in the Moonlight," which are fairly commonly available on 45 RPM. Records released after these two big hits are now worth $5 to $10.

DISCOGRAPHY

Natural
    5000   "It's Too Soon to Know"/"Barbara Lee"
           (also on Jubilee 5000)   1948

Jubilee

5001	"To Be with You"/"Dare to Dream"	
5001	"To Be with You"/"Lonely Christmas"	
5002	"Please Give My Heart a Break"/"It Seems So Long Ago"	1949
5005	"Tell Me So"/"Deacon Jones"	
5008	"I Challenge Your Kiss"/"Donkey Serenade"	
5009	"A Kiss and a Rose"/"It's a Cold Summer"	
5016	"Forgive and Forget"/"So Much"	
5017	"What Are You Doing New Year's Eve"/"Lonely Christmas"	
5018	"Would You Still Be the One"/"Is My Heart Wasting Time"	1950
5025	"At Night"/"Every Dog Gone Time"	
5028	"You're Gone"/"Everything They Said Came True"	
5031	"I'd Rather Have You Under the Moon"/"We're Supposed to Be Through"	
5037	"I Need You So"/"Goodnight Irene"	
5040	"I Cross My Fingers"/"Can't Seem to Laugh Anymore"	
5045	"Oh Holy Night"/"The Lord's Prayer"	
5051	"I Miss You So"/"You Are My First Love"	1951
5055	"Pal of Mine"/"Happy Go Lucky Local Blues"	
5057	"When You're a Long Long Way from Home"/"Would I Love You"	
5061	"I'm Just a Fool in Love"/"Hold Me, Squeeze Me"	
5065	"Baby Please Don't Go"/"Don't Tell Her What's Happened to Me"	
5071	"How Blind Can You Be"/"When You're Not Around"	
5074	"Trust in Me"/"Shrimp Boats"	1952
5076	"Proud of You"/"You Never Cared for Me"	
5082	"Waiting"/"It's All Over Because We're Through"	
5082	"Barfly"/"Getting Tired, Tired, Tired"	
5092	"See See Rider"/"Don't Cry, Baby"	

5102	"You Belong to Me"/"I Don't Want to Take a Chance"	
5107	"Till Then"/"I Miss You So"	1953
5108	"Teardrops on My Pillow"/"Hold Me, Thrill Me, Kiss Me"	
5115	"Dem Days"/"Bad Little Girl"	
5120	"I Cover the Waterfront"/"One More Time"	
5122	"Crying in the Chapel"/"Don't You Think I Ought to Know"	
5127	"Write and Tell Me Why"/"In the Mission of St. Augustine"	
5134	"Robe of Calvary"/"There's No One but You"	1953
5137	"Don't Go to Strangers"/"Secret Love"	1954
5143	"Maybe You'll Be There"/"Drowning Every Hope I Ever Had"	
5154	"In the Chapel in the Moonlight"/"Take the Lord, Thank the Lord"	
5161	"If You Believe"/"Longing"	
5172	"Count Your Blessings Instead of Sheep"/"Runaround"	
5177	"I Love You Mostly"/"Fair Exchange"	1955
5189	"I Need You Baby"/"The Good Lord Will Smile"	
5221	"Please Sing My Blues Tonight"/"Moody over You"	
5231	"Don't Go to Strangers"/"Angel"	1956

Vee Jay

196	"Happy Till the Letter"/"I Just Got Lucky"	1956
228	"For All We Know"/"Never Leave Me Baby"	
244	"Sugar Girl"/"Didn't I Say"	

The Robins

HISTORY AND SOUND

The Robins were one of the early second-generation rhythm and blues vocal groups. They recorded for numerous labels and throughout their career underwent constant and complicated personnel changes. Bobby Nunn was the lead singer through the Savoy, RCA and Spark era and can be heard on most of the biggest hits. The Robins are best associated with their Spark releases, "Riot in Cell Block #9," with a Richard Berry lead, and "Smokey Joe's Café." The style the group developed during this period was successfully translated into the work of the Coasters. In 1956, the Robins split into two groups—two members formed the Robins on Whippet, while Bobby Nunn, later joined by Young Jessie, formed the Coasters on Atco. As the Coasters, the group attained their first national success with "Searchin'," and on a greater scale, with "Yakety Yak." The Coaster's survived into the 60's, maintaining their comic style, which is traceable to the early Spark releases.

RARITY AND VALUE

The Savoy releases are considered rare on 45 RPM. The most common is Savoy 731, which was found recently in the Savoy warehouse and now sells for around $10. The Score, Hollywood, Aladdin and Modern releases are extremely rare on 45 RPM and bring premium prices. The early RCA recordings are also rare, generally commanding over $50, while the most common RCA 5489 can bring $20. The Crown releases are valued in the $40 range. The Spark releases, the first hit records, are valued from under $10 for "Riot in Cell Block #9" and "Framed," to over $15 for "If Teardrops Were Kisses"—a beautiful example of group harmony. The releases on Atco and Whippet are commonly found and are worth under $5.

DISCOGRAPHY

Savoy

726	"If It's So Baby"/"If I Didn't Love You So" 1949
731	"Double Crossin' Blues"/"Ain't Nothin' Shakin' "
	(with Little Esther and Johnny Otis)
732	"The Turkey Hop Pt. 1 & 2" (with Johnny Otis)
735	"Mistrusting Blues"/"Misery"
738	"Our Romance Is Gone"/"There Ain't No
	Use Beggin' "
752	"I'm Living OK"/"Rain in My Eyes" 1950
762	"I'm Through"/"You're Fine but Not My Kind"

Score

4010	"Around about Midnight"/"You Sure Look
	Good to Me"

Hollywood

112	"Race of a Man"/"Bayou Baby Blues"
150	"School Girl Blues"/"Early Morning Blues"

Aladdin

3031	"Don't Like the Way You're Doin' "/"Come
	Back Baby"

Modern

807	"Rockin' "/"The Good Book Says" 1951

RCA

5175	"A Fool Such as I"/"My Heart's the
	Biggest Fool" 1952
5271	"All Night Baby"/"Oh Why" 1953
5434	"How Would You Know"/"Let's Go to the Dance"
5489	"Ten Days in Jail"/"Empty Bottles"
5564	"Don't Stop Now"/"Get It off Your Mind" 1954

Crown

106	"I Made a Vow"/"Double Crossin' Baby"
120	"Key to My Heart"/"All I Do Is Rock"

Spark

103	"Riot in Cell Block #9"/"Wrap It Up"

107	"Framed"/"Loop De Loop Mambo"	1955
110	"If Teardrops Were Kisses"/"Whadaya Want"	
113	"One Kiss"/"I Love Paris"	
116	"I Must Be Dreamin' "/"The Hatchet Man"	
122	"Smokey Joe's Café"/"Just Like a Fool" (also on Atco 6059)	

Whippet

200	"Cherry Lips"/"Out of the Picture"	1956
201	"Merry Go Rock"/"Hurt Me"	
203	"Since I First Met You"/"That Old Black Magic"	1957
206	"A Fool in Love"/"All of a Sudden My Heart Sings"	

Knight

| 2001 | "Pretty Little Dolly"/"Quarter To Twelve" | 1958 |
| 2008 | "A Little Bird Told Me"/"It's Never Too Late" | |

As by the Coasters:

Atco

6064	"Down in Mexico"/"Turtle Dovin' "	1956
6072	"One Kiss Led to Another"/"Brazil"	
6087	"Searchin' "/"Young Blood"	
6098	"My Baby Comes to Me"/"Idol with the Golden Head"	1957
6104	"What Is the Secret of Your Success"/"Sweet Georgia Brown"	
6111	"Dance"/"Gee Golly"	1958
6116	"Yakety Yak"/"Zing Went the Strings of My Heart"	
6126	"The Shadow Knows"/"Sorry But I'm Gonna Have to Pass"	
6132	"Charlie Brown"/"Three Cool Cats"	
6141	"Along Came Jones"/"That Is Rock 'n' Roll"	1959
6146	"Poison Ivy"/"I'm a Hog for You"	

The Clovers

HISTORY AND SOUND

The Clovers were a very popular vocal group with a fine and highly distinctive style. They achieved success with their first Atlantic releases, and great success with "One Mint Julep." From that 1952 hit until 1956, the Clovers recorded some very strong records, many dealing with drinking and women, both subjects handled in a light-hearted style, for instance, "Crawlin'," "Good Lovin'" and "Lovey Dovey." The group's ballad style is apparent in the later recordings of "Devil or Angel" and "Blue Velvet."

RARITY AND VALUE

The Rainbow release is extremely rare on 45 RPM—only a bootleg version, on red vinyl, can be verified. The first two yellow Atlantic 45 RPM records are rare; "Skylark" is worth in excess of $35, "Fool, Fool, Fool" can bring over $15. "One Mint Julep" and later releases command less than $15, as they are all only fairly rare on the original yellow label. However, all of these records are consistently excellent.

DISCOGRAPHY

Rainbow
122	"Yes Sir, That's My Baby"/"When You Come Back to Me"	1950

Atlantic
934	"Skylark"/"Don't You Know I Love You"	1951
944	"Fool, Fool, Fool"/"Needless"	
963	"One Mint Julep"/"Middle of the Night"	1952

969	"Ting-A-Ling"/"Wonder Where My Baby's Gone"	
977	"I Played the Fool"/"Hey Miss Fannie"	
989	"Crawlin' "/"Yes It's You"	1953
1000	"Good Lovin' "/"Here Goes a Fool"	
1010	"Comin' On"/"The Feeling Is So Good"	
1022	"Lovey Dovey"/"Little Mama"	1954
1035	"I've Got My Eyes on You"/"Your Cash Ain't Nothing but Trash"	
1046	"I Confess"/"All Right, Oh Sweetie"	
1052	"Blue Velvet"/"If You Love Me"	
1060	"In the Morning Time"/"Lovebug"	1955
1073	"Nip Sip"/"If I Could Be Loved by You"	
1083	"Devil or Angel"/"Hey Doll Baby"	
1094	"Your Tender Lips"/"Love, Love, Love"	1956
1107	"From the Bottom of My Heart"/"Bring Me Love"	
1118	"Baby Baby, Oh My Darling"/"Lonely Fool"	
1129	"You Good-Looking Woman"/"Here Comes Romance"	1957
1139	"So Young"/"I-I-I Love You"	
1152	"Down in the Alley"/"There's No Tomorrow"	
1178	"Wishing for Your Love"/"All About You"	1958

The Dominoes

HISTORY AND SOUND

The Dominoes were a very strong 50's group, recording for the new Federal label. With the two famous alternate lead singers —Clyde McPhatter and Jackie Wilson—the group couldn't miss. The first three records were poor-sellers, but "Sixty Minute Man" was a stone smash. The group never scored that well again, but they produced great rockers with "Have Mercy Baby" and "That's What You're Doin' to Me." They recorded such fine ballads as "When the Swallows Come Back to Capistrano,"

"No Room" and "These Foolish Things Remind Me of You,"
along with their famous, highly charged "weepers," "The Bells"
and "Deep Sea Blues." Simultaneously, the group recorded
several ballads on the parent King label, showcasing Billy Ward
as a pop singer. The group suffered from these attempts at
popularizing their sound and the Jubilee, Decca and Liberty
records reflect this decline.

RARITY AND VALUE

Being poor-sellers, the first three Federal releases are very rare.
"Harbor Lights" can bring $100, the other two are worth well
over $50. "Sixty Minute Man" will bring over $10 on the
original "gold top" Federal label, and subsequent releases
(through Federal 12129) bring prices in the $20 range. The
Jubilee, Decca and Liberty releases are generally worth less
than $5.

DISCOGRAPHY

Federal

12001	"Do Something for Me"/"Chicken Blues"	1950
12010	"Harbor Lights"/"No Says My Heart"	1951
12016	"The Deacon Moves In"/"Other Lips, Other Arms" (with Little Esther)	
12022	"Sixty Minute Man"/"I Can't Escape from You"	
12036	"Heart to Heart"/"Looking for a Man" (with Little Esther)	
12039	"I Am with You"/"Weeping Willow Blues"	
12059	"When the Swallows Come Back to Capistrano"/"That's What You're Doing to Me"	1952
12068	"Have Mercy Baby"/"Deep Sea Blues"	
12072	"That's What You're Doing to Me"/"Love, Love, Love"	
12105	"No Room"/"I'd Be Satisfied"	

12106	"I'm Lonely"/"Yours Forever"	
12114	"The Bells"/"Pedal Pushin' Papa"	
12129	"These Foolish Things Remind Me of You"/ "Don't Leave Me This Way"	1953
12139	"You Can't Keep a Good Man Down"/"Where Now Little Heart"	
12162	"Until the Real Thing Comes Along"/"My Baby's 3-D"	
12178	"I'm Gonna Move to the Outskirts of Town"/ "Tootsie Roll"	1954
12184	"Handwriting on the Wall"/"One Moment with You"	
12193	"Above Jacob's Ladder"/"Little Black Train"	
12209	"If I Never Get to Heaven"/"Can't Do Sixty No More"	1955
12218	"Love Me Now or Let Me Go"/"Cave Man"	
12263	"How Long, How Long Blues"/"Bobby Sox Baby"	
12301	"One Moment with You"/"St. Louis Blues"	
12308	"Have Mercy Baby"/"Love, Love, Love"	

King

1280	"Rags to Riches"/"Don't Thank Me"	1954
1281	"Bringing in a Brand New Year"/"Christmas in Heaven"	
1342	"Tenderly"/"A Little Lie"	1955
1364	"Three Coins in the Fountain"/"Lonesome Road"	
1368	"Little Things Mean a Lot"/"I Really Don't Want to Know"	
1492	"May I Never Love Again"/"Learning the Blues"	
1502	"Over the Rainbow"/"Give Me You"	

Jubilee

| 5163 | "Gimme, Gimme, Gimme"/"Come to Me, Baby" | |
| 5213 | "Sweethearts on Parade"/"Take Me Back to Heaven" | |

Decca

| 29933 | "St. Therese of the Roses"/"Home Is Where You Hang Your Heart" | 1956 |

30043	"Will You Remember"/"Come on Snake, Let's Crawl"	
30149	"Evermore"/"Half a Love"	1957
30420	"I Don't Stand a Ghost of a Chance with You"/ "To Each His Own"	
30514	"September Song"/"When the Saints Go Marching In"	

Liberty

55071	"Stardust"/"Lucinda"	
55099	"Deep Purple"/"Do It Again"	
55111	"My Proudest Possession"/"Someone Greater Than I"	
55126	"Sweeter as the Years Go By"/"Solitude"	1958
55136	"Jennie Lee"/"Music, Maestro, Please"	
55181	"Please Don't Say No"/"Behave, Hula Girl"	

The Hollywood Flames

HISTORY AND SOUND

This group was originally called the Flames, then the Hollywood 4 Flames, finally the Hollywood Flames. During their early career, they recorded some excellent, yet poor-selling records. Their versions of "Wheel of Fortune" and "Tabarin" are considered classics by current collectors. Their early Hollywood and Swingtime label recordings have a distinct blues sound. The first commercial success was the 1957 hit, "Buzz, Buzz, Buzz." The Ebb releases are pale commercial records in comparison to the Hollywood Flames' earlier records.

RARITY AND VALUE

All of the very early records by the Hollywood 4 Flames must be considered very rare on 45 RPM. Several are available as bootlegs. The Lucky, Swingtime and Specialty releases are also very rare, bringing prices of $45 and more. The Money release is worth about $30, the Ebb releases generally under $5.

DISCOGRAPHY

As by the Hollywood 4 Flames:
Hollywood

164	"I'll Always Be a Fool"/"She's Got Something"	1950
165AA	"Baby Please"	
165A	"Young Girl"	
165B	"Glory of Love"	

Unique

003	"Dividend Blues"/"W-I-N-E"	1951
005	"Tabarin"/"Cry for My Baby"	
015	"Please Say I'm Wrong"/"The Masquerade Is Over"	

As by the Flames:
Specialty

429	"The Wheel of Fortune"/"Later"	1952

As by the Hollywood Flames:
Lucky

001	"One Night with a Fool"/"Ride, Helen, Ride"	1952
006	"Peggy"/"Oooh La La" (also on Decca 48331)	

Swingtime

345	"Let's Talk It Over"/"I Know" (also on Decca 29285)	1953

Money

202	"Fare Thee Well"/"Clickety Clack, I'm Leaving"	1954

Ebb

119	"Buzz, Buzz, Buzz"/"Crazy"	1957
131	"Give Me Back My Heart"/"A Little Bird"	

The Cardinals

HISTORY AND SOUND

Though the Cardinals were promoted along with the Clovers by Atlantic records, the group never achieved the enormous success of the Clovers. Their "Wheel of Fortune" is considered the definitive rhythm and blues version of the song, and "The Door Is Still Open" is a fine harmonious rendition of that standard. In fact, the Cardinals never recorded a poor or average record.

RARITY AND VALUE

All of the early releases by the group are rare. The first three, being the rarest, generally bring over $40. "The Door Is Still Open" and "Come Back My Love" were the biggest hits and are now worth under $20.

DISCOGRAPHY

Atlantic

958   "Wheel of Fortune"/"Shouldn't I Know"
972   "She Rocks"/"The Bump"   1952
995   "Lovie Darling"/"You Are My Only Love"   1953
1025   "Please Baby"/"Blanket of Blue"   1954
1054   "The Door Is Still Open"/"Misirlou"
1067   "Come Back My Love"/"Two Things I Love"   1955
1079   "Lovely Girl"/"Here Goes My Heart to You"
1090   "Off Shore"/"Choo Choo"
1103   "I Won't Make You Cry Anymore"/"The End
          of the Story"
1126   "One Love"/"Near You"

The Swallows

HISTORY AND SOUND

The Swallows had a very short recording career, but during that period managed to produce only consistently fine ballad and jump records. Their slow ballads, such as "Beside You" and "Tell Me Why," feature the effective blues vocals of lead Junior Denby. Their rhythm records, especially the classic, off-color "It Ain't the Meat," were also great. The Swallows were a rare group in that they managed to issue records of consistently high quality. It is unfortunate their career was so short.

RARITY AND VALUE

The Swallows' records are all rare. The early releases, especially the first three, are extremely rare on 45 RPM. In fact, "Wishing for You" has recently been bootlegged. An original would probably bring $100. Other later records are worth at least $50. It should be noted that the King subsidiary, Federal Records, released some records by a poor rock and roll group also named the Swallows. These should be avoided.

DISCOGRAPHY

King

4458	"Will You Be Mine"/"Dearest"	1951
4466	"Wishing for You"/"Since You've Been Away"	
4501	"Eternally"/"It Ain't the Meat"	
4515	"Tell Me Why"/"Roll, Roll, Pretty Baby"	1952
4525	"Beside You"/"You Left Me"	
4533	"I Only Have Eyes for You"/"You Walked In"	
4579	"Please, Baby, Please"/"Where Do I Go from Here"	
4612	"Laugh"/"Our Love Is Dying"	1953
4632	"Bicycle Tillie"/"Nobody's Loving Me"	
4653	"Pleading Blues"/"Trust Me"	
4676	"It Feels So Good"/"I'll Be Waiting"	1954

The Five Keys

HISTORY AND SOUND

The Five Keys, an early Aladdin Records vocal group, did very well with their second release, "Glory of Love." The other Aladdin releases sold poorly, and apparently several, including "Darling," may have been withdrawn prior to, or shortly after, release. The group specialized in the love ballad—"Teardrops in My Eyes" and "My Saddest Hour" are two of the best rhythm and blues love songs released in the 50's. The group's rhythm records, such as "Hucklebuck with Jimmy" and "I'm So High" are excellent. The Five Keys achieved their first continuous success with Capitol Records. In the process, they lost some of their spontaneity, and the price they paid for commercial acceptance was use of middle-of-the-road orchestration. The most successful Capitol releases were "Ling Ting Tong," "Close

Your Eyes," "Out of Sight, Out of Mind" and "Wisdom of a Fool." Even though the Five Keys adopted a more pop style on these Capitol releases, they are still very good records.

RARITY AND VALUE

Although "Glory of Love" sold a reported million copies, it is still very rare, and worth around $40. Other Aladdin releases are also extremely rare—"With a Broken Heart," "Darling" and "Red Sails in the Sunset" are three records that can command $100. Many of the rarer Aladdin issues and some unreleased material have recently been bootlegged and now sell for $2 or $3. The Five Keys on Aladdin are, perhaps, the group most sought after by rhythm and blues collectors. The Capitol releases are not rare, bringing prices slightly under $10.

DISCOGRAPHY

Aladdin

3085	"With a Broken Heart"/"Too Late"	1951
3099	"Glory of Love"/"Hucklebuck with Jimmy"	
3113	"Christmas Time"/"Old McDonald"	
3118	"Yes Sir, That's My Baby"/"Old McDonald"	1952
3119	"Darling"/"Goin' Downtown"	
3127	"Red Sails in the Sunset"/"Be Anything but Be Mine"	
3131	"Mistakes"/"How Long"	
3136	"I Hadn't Anyone till You"/"Hold Me"	
3158	"Serve Another Round"/"I Cried for You"	
3167	"Can't Keep from Crying"/"Come Go My Bail, Louise"	1953
3175	"There Ought to Be a Law"/"Mama"	
3182	"I'll Always Be in Love with You"/"Rocking and Crying Blues"	

3190	"These Foolish Things"/"Lonesome Old Story"
3204	"Teardrops in My Eyes"/"I'm So High"
3214	"My Saddest Hour"/"Oh Babe"
3228	"Someday Sweetheart"/"Love My Loving" 1954
3245	"Deep in My Heart"/"How Do You Expect Me to Get It"
3263	"My Love"/"Why Oh Why"
3312	"Story of Love"/"Serve Another Round"

Capitol

2945	"Ling Ting Tong"/"I'm Alone" 1954
3032	"Close Your Eyes"/"Doggone It, You Did It" 1955
3127	"The Verdict"/"Me Make Um Pow Wow"
3185	"Don't You Know I Love You"/"I Wish I'd Never Learned to Read"
3267	"Gee Whittakers"/"Cause You're My Lover"
3318	"What Goes On"/"You Broke the Rules of Love" 1956
3392	"She's the Most"/"I Dreamed I Dwelt in Heaven"
3455	"Peace and Love"/"My Pigeon's Gone"
3502	"Out of Sight, Out of Mind"/"That's Right"
3597	"Wisdom of a Fool"/"Now Don't That Prove I Love You" 1957
3660	"Let There Be You"/"Tiger Lily"
3710	"Four Walls"/"It's a Groove"
3738	"This I Promise"/"The Blues Don't Care"
3786	"The Face of an Angel"/"Boom Boom"
3830	"Do Anything"/"It's a Crying Shame" 1958
3861	"From Me to You"/"Whippety Whirl"
3948	"With All My Love"/"You're for Me"
4009	"Emily Please"/"Handy Andy"

Jesse Belvin

HISTORY AND SOUND

Jesse Belvin, though a single artist, recorded some of the 50's best vocal group-style recordings. The earliest featured Belvin as the lead singer of the Three Dots and a Dash, with Big Jay McNeeley shown on the label as featured artist. The sound of this early record is strictly upbeat rhythm and blues. The Hollywood label releases are both excellent group efforts. "Beware," on the Hollywood subsidiary label, Cash, is one of the great mellow group vocals of the era. It is Jesse Belvin at his best. The Specialty releases are all good; "Dream Girl," recorded with Marvin Phillips (later of Marvin and Johnny), is a much tighter version than the Hollywood label release. "Where's My Girl" features some fine group backing by the Feathers. The Federal release by the Sheiks is the original recording of Johnny Otis' classic "So Fine"—the reverse side is a particularly lovely ballad. The Modern label releases are very good ("Girl of My Dreams") to disappointing ("You Send Me"/"Summertime"); the latter two were covers of Sam Cooke's best-sellers. The RCA recordings reflect an attempt to turn Belvin into a pop singer. Jesse Belvin's last releases before his tragic death do not reflect his incredible talents.

RARITY AND VALUE

The Imperial and Hollywood records are very rare, but with the exception of "Dear Heart," are not as highly prized by collectors as are other group records, because Jesse Belvin is shown as single artist on the label. (Record collectors are often very shortsighted.) "Beware" was a consistent seller and thus is only fairly rare. The Specialty releases are fairly rare, generally bringing slightly under $10. Recently several of the Specialty releases have been available from dealers for less than $2, as a warehouse stock was discovered. "So Fine" is rare and can bring $20. The Modern and RCA releases usually command less than $5. The Candelite release is a well-distributed bootleg, usually selling for $1 or less.

DISCOGRAPHY

Imperial
5115   "All That Wine Is Gone"/"Don't Cry Baby"   1951
Hollywood
120   "Dream Girl"/"Hang Your Tears Out to Dry"
412   "Love Comes Tumbling Down"
       (also on Candelite 427 as "Love Song")
1059   "Dear Heart"/"Betty My Darling"
Specialty
435   "Confusin' Blues"/"Baby Don't Go"   1952
447   "Dream Girl"/"Daddy Loves Baby"   1953
       (as by Jesse and Marvin)
550   "Gone"/"One Little Blessing"   1955
559   "Where's My Girl"/"Love Love of My Life"
Federal
12237   "So Fine"/"Sentimental Heart" (as by the Sheiks)
Money
208   "I'm Only a Fool"/"Trouble and Misery"
Cash
1056   "Beware"/"Dry Your Eyes"   1956
Modern
987   "Girl of My Dreams"/"I Wanna Know Why"
       (as by the Cliques)
1005   "Goodnight My Love"/"Let Me Love You
       Tonight"
1005   "Goodnight My Love"/"I Want You with Me
       Christmas"
1013   "Senorita"/"I Need You So"   1957

1015	"Don't Close the Door"/"By My Side"	
1020	"Sad and Lonesome"/"I'm Not Free"	
1025	"You Send Me"/"Summertime"	
1027	"Just to Say Hello"/"My Satellite"	

Kent

326	"Sentimental Reasons"/"Senorita"	1958

Class

267	"Deep in My Heart"/"I'm Confessin' "

Aladdin

3431	"Sugar Doll"/"Let Me Dream"

RCA

7310	"Ever Since We Met"/"Volare"	
7387	"Funny"/"Pledging My Love"	
7469	"Guess Who"/"My Girl Is Just Enough Woman for Me"	1959
7543	"It Could've Been Worse"/"Here's a Heart"	
7596	"Give Me Love"/"I'll Never Be Lonely Again"	

The Five Royales

HISTORY AND SOUND

Originally a gospel group called the Royal Sons, the renamed Five Royales carried a shouting gospel-tinged style to their rhythm and blues recordings. Their earliest hit, "Baby Don't Do It," sold well and gave origin to several "answer" records by other groups. The Five Royales' aggressive style is also evident in "Dedicated to the One I Love" (a 1961 hit record for the Shirelles).

RARITY AND VALUE

Although some of the group's early Apollo recordings are rare, they do not attract collectors' interest, and thus value, as do records by sweeter-sounding vocal groups. Therefore the Apollo and King recordings, which are the rarest, bring less than $10.

DISCOGRAPHY

As by the Royal Sons:
Apollo
    253   "Beside of a Neighbor"/"Journey's End"   c. 1948
    266   "Come Over Here"/"Let Nothing Separate Me"
As by the Royalls:
Apollo
    434   "Too Much of a Little Bit"/"Give Me One
              More Chance"   1952
As by the Five Royales:
Apollo
    441   "Courage to Love"/"I Know You Know"
    443   "Baby Don't Do It"/"Take All of Me"
    446   "Crazy, Crazy, Crazy"/"Help Me Somebody" 1953
    448   "Too Much Lovin' "/"Laundromat Blues"
    449   "I Want to Thank You"/"All Righty"
    452   "I Do"/"Good Things"
    454   "Cry Some More"/I Like It Like That"
    458   "Let Me Come Back Home"/"What's That"
    461   "Six O'Clock in the Morning"/"With All
              Your Heart"
King
    4740   "Behave Yourself"/"I'm Gonna Run
              It Down"   1954
    4744   "Monkey Hips and Rice"/"Devil with the Rest"
    4762   "School Girl"/"One Mistake"
    4770   "You Didn't Learn It at Home"/"Every Dog
              Has His Day"   1955
    4785   "How I Wonder"/"Mohawk Squaw"
    4806   "I Need Your Lovin' Baby"/"When I Get
              Like This"

4819	"Women about to Make You Go Crazy"/ "Do unto You"	
4830	"Somebody Made You for Me"/"Ain't Gettin' Caught"	
4869	"When You Walked through the Door"/ "Right around the Corner"	1956
4901	"I Could Love You"/"My Wants for You"	
4952	"Come on and Save Me"/"Get Something out of It"	
4973	"Just as I Am"/"Mine Forevermore"	1957
5032	"Tears of Joy"/"Thirty Second Lover"	
5053	"Think"/"I'd Better Make a Move"	
5082	"Messin' Up"/"Say It"	1958
5098	"Dedicated to the One I Love"/"Don't Be Ashamed"	
5131	"Do the Cha Cha Cherry"/"The Feeling Is Real"	
5141	"Tell the Truth"/"Double or Nothing"	1959
5153	"Don't Let It Be in Vain"/"The Slummer the Slum"	
5162	"The Real Thing"/"Your Only Love"	

The Royals

HISTORY AND SOUND

The Royals' first record, Johnny Otis' composition "Every Beat of My Heart" (a 1961 hit record for Gladys Knight and the Pips), was a fine ballad, producing negligible chart action for the group. The Royals recorded other ballads but were unable to release a hit record. They then hit upon on successful formula with "Get It," a jump record with sexually oriented lyrics. "Work with Me Annie" was drawn from "Get It," and attracted widespread attention to the Royals. In fact, King Records tried to withdraw that "dirty" record, but the public's favorable reaction forced distribution of the disc. The Royals were renamed the Midnighters to avoid confusion with the Five Royales, just signed by King. From the point that the group became the Midnighters, with Hank Ballard as lead vocalist, they produced a string of very successful follow-up "Annie" records—essentially "Work with Me Annie," with slightly varied lyrics. Other groups, including the Midnights, the El Dorados and the Platters, recorded answers to the "Annie" records. Etta James with Richard Berry recorded "The Wallflower" ("Roll with Me Henry") taken from "Work with Me Annie." "The Wallflower" was also considered off-color in certain quarters; thus, in turn, the cover record, "Dance with Me Henry" by Georgia Gibbs, was released by Mercury Records. This diluted version finally reduced "Work with Me Annie" to harmless and innocuous respectability. Hank Ballard continued with the Midnighters to the late 50's and early 60's, having the later hit "Finger Poppin' Time" and the mild seller "The Twist" in 1959.

RARITY AND VALUE

The first six Federal releases are very rare ballads, much sought after by collectors, bringing prices from $50 to $75. Later records by the Royals are also rare, but are not in such demand, and thus their value probably does not exceed $20. The Midnighters' records were good sellers, and thus are only fairly rare, worth close to $10 at best. Recently, a mythical (?) Midnighters' disc entitled "Annie Had a Miscarriage" has been rumored and now has become a prime collectors' want. (Rumors of rarity do create value.)

DISCOGRAPHY

Federal
  12064   "Every Beat of My Heart"/"All Night Long" 1952
  12077   "Starting from Tonight"/"I Know I Love You So"

12088   "Moonrise"/"Fifth St. Blues"
12098   "I'll Never Let Her Go"/"A Love in My Heart"
12113   "Are You Forgetting"/"What Did I Do"
12121   "The Shrine of St. Cecilia"/"I Feel So Blue"   1953
12133   "Get It"/"No It Ain't"
12150   "I Feel That a Way"/"Hello Miss Fine"
12160   "Someone Like You"/"That's It"
12169   "Work with Me Annie"/"Until I Die"
12177   "Give It Up"/"That Woman"
         (Federal 12169 and 12177 also issued by the
         Midnighters)

As by the Midnighters:
Federal
12185   "Sexy Ways"/"Don't Say Your Last Goodbye"   1954
12195   "Annie Had a Baby"/"She's the One"
12200   "Annie's Aunt Fanny"/"Crazy Loving"
12202   "Stingy Little Thing"/"Tell Them"
12205   "Moonrise"/"She's the One"   1955
12210   "Ring-A-Ling-A-Ling"/"Ashamed of Myself"
12220   "Switchie Witchie Titchie"/"Why Are We Apart"
12224   "Henry's Got Flat Feet"/"Whatsonever You Do"
12227   "It's Love Baby"/"Looka Here"
12230   "Give It Up"/"That Woman"
12240   "That House on the Hill"/"Rock and Roll
         Wedding"
12243   "Don't Change Your Pretty Ways"/"We'll Never
         Meet Again"
12251   "Sweet Mama Do Right"/"Partners for Life"   1956
12260   "Open up the Back Door"/"Rock Granny Roll"
12270   "Tore up over You"/"Early One Morning"
12285   "I'll Be Home Some Day"/"Come on a Get It"
12288   "Let Me Hold Your Hand"/"Ooh Bah Baby"   1957
12293   "In the Doorway Crying"/"E Basta Cosi"
12299   "Oh So Happy"/"Is Your Love for Real"

12305	"Let 'Em Roll"/"What Made You Change Your Mind"	
12317	"Daddy's Little Baby"/"Stay by My Side"	
12339	"Baby Please"/"Ow Wow Oo Wee"	1958

King

5171	"The Twist"/"Teardrops on Your Letter"	1959
5195	"Kansas City"/"I'll Keep You Happy"	
5215	"Sugaree"/"Rain Down Tears"	
5245	"House with No Windows"/"Cute Little Ways"	
5289	"Look at Little Sister"/"I Said I Wouldn't Beg You"	
5312	"The Coffee Grind"/"Waiting"	
5341	"Finger Poppin' Time"/"I Love You, I Love You So-o-o"	

The Checkers

HISTORY AND SOUND

The Checkers were apparently signed by King Records to cash in on the success of the similarly named Dominoes. In fact, several members of the group were drawn from the Dominoes. One of the Checkers' releases, "Don't Stop Dan," is an answer record to the Dominoes' "Sixty Minute Man." Fortunately the Checkers were an excellent group in their own right. Their best record is the haunting ballad "House with No Windows." However, the group's most successful record was the uptempo "White Cliffs of Dover."

RARITY AND VALUE

The rarest Checkers records are the first five releases. The first three can bring $40 to $50, the next two are worth over $25. Even "White Cliffs of Dover" can bring from $15 to $20.

DISCOGRAPHY

4558	"Flame in My Heart"/"Oh Oh Oh Baby"	1952
4581	"Nights Curtains"/"Let Me Come Back"	
4596	"My Prayer Tonite"/"Love Wasn't There"	1953
4626	"Ghost of My Baby"/"I Wanna Know"	
4673	"You Never Had It So Good"/"I Promise You"	1954
4675	"White Cliffs of Dover"/"Without a Song"	
4710	"House with No Windows"/"Don't Stop Dan"	
4719	"Over the Rainbow"/"You've Been Fooling Around"	
4751	"I Wasn't Thinkin', I Was Drinkin' "/ "Mama's Daughter"	
4764	"Can't Find My Sadie"/"Tryin' to Hold My Gal"	1955
5156	"Heaven Only Knows"/"Nine More Miles"	1958
5199	"Teardrops Are Falling"/"Rocka Locka"	1959

The Moonglows

HISTORY AND SOUND

The Moonglows' solitary Champagne release is an excellent, but little known, vocal group release. The Chance recordings are uniformly good performances. None of these early releases sold well. The Moonglows' first hit of any stature was a song written by lead singer Harvey Fuqua and disc jockey Allen Freed (who coined the term "rock and roll"). The song was "Sincerely." It became one of the great rhythm and blues standards of the 50's. The Moonglows capitalized on their popularity by releasing several good-selling follow-ups, including

"Most of All," "In My Diary" and "We Go Together," all very fine ballads. However, even the next big hit, "Ten Commandments of Love," with Fuqua's syrupy pronouncement of the commandments, did not approach the immense success of "Sincerely."

RARITY AND VALUE

The Champagne and Chance records qualify as very rare discs. They are all sweetly sung ballads and thus are in great demand. "I Just Can't Tell No Lie" will bring $75; "219 Train," the rarest Chance, commands $100. "I Was Wrong," the least rare Chance, still is worth around $40. The Chess releases are worth under $10.

DISCOGRAPHY

Champagne
| 7500 | "I Just Can't Tell No Lie"/"I've Been Your Dog" | 1952 |

Chance
1147	"Baby Please"/"Whistle My Love"	1953
1150	"Just a Lonely Christmas"/"Hey Santa Claus"	
1152	"Secret Love"/"Real Gone Mama"	1954
1156	"I Was Wrong"/"Ooh Rocking Daddy"	
1161	"219 Train"/"My Gal"	

Chess
1581	"Sincerely"/"Tempting"	
1589	"Most of All"/"She's Gone"	
1598	"Foolish Me"/"Slow Down"	1955
1605	"Starlite"/"In Love"	
1611	"In My Diary"/"Lover Love Me"	
1619	"We Go Together"/"Chickie Um Bah"	1956
1629	"When I'm with You"/"See Saw"	

1646   "Over and Over Again"/"I Knew from the Start"
1651   "I'm Afraid the Masquerade Is Over"/"Don't
        Say Goodbye"
1661   "Please Send Me Someone to Love"/"Mr.
        Engineer"   1957
1669   "The Beating of My Heart"/"Confess It to
        Your Heart"
1681   "Too Late"/"Here I Am"
1689   "In the Middle of the Night"/"Soda Pop"   1958
1701   "This Love"/"Sweeter Than Words"
1705   "Ten Commandments of Love"/"Mean Old Blues"
1717   "I'll Never Stop Wanting You"/"Love Is a
        River"   1959
1738   "Mama Loocie"/"Unemployment"

The Drifters

HISTORY AND SOUND

The Drifters were the third major Atlantic Records vocal group
(signed after the Clovers and the Cardinals), and equaled the
Clovers in popularity. The group, originally with a Clyde Mc-
Phatter (of Dominoes fame) lead, first clicked with the upbeat,
compelling "Money Honey." In fact, every record by the
Drifters, especially "Honey Love" and "White Christmas" (a
hit for several Christmases), was a success. Most of the group's
recordings were in a driving jump tempo. The group, re-formed,
with a Ben E. King lead, scored their biggest smash with "There
Goes My Baby," one of the first rhythm and blues releases to
use strings as accompaniment.

RARITY AND VALUE

None of the recordings by the Drifters have unusual value.
The group performed few ballads, thus none of their records is
worth in excess of $10. "Money Honey" is the rarest.

DISCOGRAPHY

Atlantic

1006	"Money Honey"/"The Way I Feel"	1953
1019	"Such a Night"/"Lucille"	
1029	"Honey Love"/"Warm Your Heart"	1954
1043	"Bip Bam"/"Someday You'll Want Me to Want You"	
1048	"White Christmas"/"The Bells of St. Mary's"	
1055	"Gone"/"What'cha Gonna Do"	1955
1078	"Adorable"/"Steamboat"	
1089	"Ruby Baby"/"Your Promise to Be Mine"	
1101	"Soldier of Fortune"/"I Got to Get Myself a Woman"	1956
1123	"It Was a Tear"/"Fools Fall in Love"	
1141	"Hypnotized"/"Drifting Away from You"	1957
1161	"I Know"/"Yodee Yakee"	
1187	"Drip Drop"/"Moonlight Bay"	1958
2025	"There Goes My Baby"/"Oh My Love"	1959
2040	"Dance with Me"/"True Love, True Love"	

The Charms

HISTORY AND SOUND

The Charms were a very hot 50's vocal group. Their earliest releases on Rockin' and DeLuxe were love ballads. However, the group clicked with the uptempo style of their sixth record, "Hearts of Stone." It was this rock and roll format that proved successful and provided the Charms with a string of ten or twelve hits. Later records also sold fairly well for the Charms and lead singer Otis Williams.

RARITY AND VALUE

The five early releases are very rare and are the most sought after, bringing prices from $30 to $50. Later rock and roll releases bring less than $10.

DISCOGRAPHY

Rockin'
516	"Heaven Only Knows"/"Loving Baby" (also on DeLuxe 6000)	1953

DeLuxe
6014	"Happy Are We"/"What Do You Know about That"	
6034	"Please Believe in Me"/"Bye Bye Baby"	1954
6050	"Quiet Please"/"Fifty-Five Seconds"	
6056	"My Baby Dearest Darling"/"Come to Me Baby"	
6062	"Hearts of Stone"/"Who Knows"	
6065	"Two Hearts"/"The First Time We Met"	
6072	"Crazy, Crazy Love"/"Mambo Sh Mambo"	
6080	"Ko Ko Mo"/"Whadaya Want"	1955
6082	"Crazy, Crazy Love"/"Whadaya Want"	
6087	"When We Get Together"/"Let the Happening Happen"	
6088	"Miss the Love"/"Tell Me Now"	
6089	"One Fine Day"/"It's You, Yes You"	
6090	"Gum Drop"/"Save Me, Save Me"	
6091	"That's Your Mistake"/"Too Late I Learned"	
6092	"Rollin' Home"/"Do Be You"	1956
6093	"Ivory Tower"/"In Paradise"	
6095	"It's All Over"/"One Night Only"	
6097	"Whirlwind"/"I'd Like to Thank You Mr. D. J."	
6098	"Gypsy Lady"/"I'll Remember You"	
6105	"Pardon Me"/"Blues Stay Away from Me"	1957

6115	"Walkin' after Midnight"/"I'm Waiting Just for You"	
6130	"Nowhere on Earth"/"No Got De Woman"	
6138	"United"/"Don't Deny Me"	
6149	"Well Oh Well"/"Dynamite Darling"	
6158	"Could This Be Magic"/"Oh Julie"	1958
6160	"Let Some Love in Your Heart"/"Baby O"	
6165	"Burnin' Lips"/"Red Hot Love"	
6174	"You'll Remain Forever"/"Don't Wake up the Kids"	
6178	"My Friends"/"Secret"	
6181	"Welcome Home"/"Pretty Little Things Called Girls"	
6183	"My Prayer Tonight"/"Watch Dog"	

Chart

608	"Love's Our Inspiration"/"Love Love Stick Stov"	1955
613	"Heart of a Rose"/"I Offer You"	
623	"I'll Be True"/"Boom Diddy Boom Boom"	

The Crows

HISTORY AND SOUND

The Crows are most widely associated with their second record, the first major rhythm and blues hit with a jump beat, and a forerunner of the label's rock and roll style—"Gee." However, the group's other Rama releases were every bit as good as "Gee," but were largely unknown and unsold. "Mambo Shevitz" was a poor record, a takeoff on a popular radio jingle for Manishevitz Wine.

RARITY AND VALUE

"Gee" is worth about $10, unless on red vinyl, which adds about $15 to the price. The other recordings are worth about $50.

"Seven Lonely Days" is the rarest of the lot, worth around $100, again on colored vinyl.

DISCOGRAPHY

Rama

3	"Seven Lonely Days"/"No Help Wanted"	1953
5	"Gee"/"I Love You So"	
10	"Heartbreaker"/"Call a Doctor"	
29	"Untrue"/"Baby"	1954
30	"Miss You"/"I Really Really Love You"	
50	"Baby Doll"/"Sweet Sue"	

Tico

1082	"Mambo Shevitz"/"Mambo #5"	

The Harptones

HISTORY AND SOUND

The Harptones, with Winnie Winfield singing lead, first recorded in 1953. The group's versions of the standards "Sunday Kind of Love" and "Memories of You" have become 50's vocal group classics. Though not instant hits at the point of release, these two were among the most consistently selling records of the decade. After the Bruce recordings, the group had releases on several small labels. All of these recordings were excellent, mellow ballads. The Harptones began as a ballad group, never experimented with jump or rock and roll songs, and maintained consistent success.

RARITY AND VALUE

The original issues of the Bruce recordings are now rare, and the purists' insistence on the original makes these issues fairly valuable, even though reissues with slightly different label print are now commonly found. Later releases are fairly valuable, often bringing $10 to $20.

DISCOGRAPHY

Bruce

101	"Sunday Kind of Love"/"I'll Never Tell"	1953
102	"My Memories of You"/"It Was Just for Laughs"	1954
104	"I Depended on You"/"Mambo Boogie"	
109	"Forever Mine"/"Why Should I Love You"	
113	"Since I Fell for You"/"Oobidee Oobidee Oo"	
123	"Loving a Girl Like You"/"High Flyin' Baby"	
128	"I Almost Lost My Mind"/"Oo Wee Baby"	1955

Essex

364	"I'll Never Tell"/"Honey Love" (with Bunny Paul)

Paradise

101	"Life Is But a Dream"/"You Know You're Doing Me Wrong"
103	"It All Depends on You"/"Guitar Shuffle"

Rama

203	"Three Wishes"/"That's the Way It Goes"	1956
214	"The Masquerade Is Over"/"On a Sunday Afternoon"	
221	"The Shrine of St. Cecilia"/"Oo Wee Baby"	

Andrea

100	"What Is Your Decision"/"Gimme Some"

Raven

8001	"Sunday Kind of Love"/"Mambo Boogie"

Tip Top
    401   "Memories of You"/"High Flyin' Baby"
Gee
    1045   "Cry Like I Cried"/"So Good, So Fine"   1957

The Flamingos

HISTORY AND SOUND

The Flamingos specialized in the romantic ballad, and were the leading exponent of that style in the 50's. The group, which never radically changed their format or method of expression, managed to attract increasing attention and sales with each label switch. However, the earliest Chance and Parrot recordings, especially "Golden Teardrops" and "Dream of a Lifetime," are considered the Flamingos' best and are among the most sought after by collectors. The first four Checker label releases are superb love songs and provided the group with its first chart action. However, it was the End label releases that put the Flamingos in the top forty. Their biggest hit was "I Only Have Eyes for You," and the unusual arrangement put the record over. That was the apex. Later records sold well, but never quite as well. However, the group continued to use the lush arrangements characteristic of "Lovers Never Say Goodbye" and "I Only Have Eyes for You" and maintained a consistent following.

RARITY AND VALUE

The Flamingos' recordings are an example of the widely varying prices records by the same vocal group can attract. The Chance and Parrot discs bring top prices, usually $50 and up. "I Really Don't Want to Know" ranks among the rarest of all records, commanding in excess of $100. "Dream of a Lifetime" (one of the earliest group records to be bootlegged) brings around $15 on black vinyl, around $50 on red vinyl. The Checker recordings bring around $10, the End releases are worth less than $5, since they were all very good sellers. None of these prices reflects on the validity of the record, just the availability.

DISCOGRAPHY

Chance
1133	"If I Can't Have You"/"Someday Someway"	1953
1140	"That's My Desire"/"Hurry Home Baby"	
1145	"Golden Teardrops"/"Carried Away"	
1149	"Plan for Love"/"You Ain't Ready"	
1154	"Cross over the Bridge"/"Listen to My Plea"	1954
1162	"Blues in a Letter"/"Jump Children"	

Parrot
808	"Dream of a Lifetime"/"On My Merry Way"
811	"I Really Don't Want to Know"/"Get with It"
812	"I'm Yours"/"Ko Ko Mo"

Checker
815	"When"/"That's My Baby"	1955
821	"Please Come Back Home"/"I Want to Love You"	
830	"I'll Be Home"/"Need Your Love"	1956
837	"A Kiss from Your Lips"/"Get with It"	
846	"The Vow"/"Shilly Dilly"	
853	"Would I Be Crying"/"Just for a Kick"	
915	"Dream of a Lifetime"/"Whispering Stars"	1959
1084	"Lover Come Back to Me"/"Your Little Guy"	

Decca
30335	"The Ladder of Love"/"Let's Make Up"	1957
30454	"My Faith in You"/"Helpless"	
30687	"Where Mary Go"/"Rock and Roll March"	
30880	"Kiss a Me"/"Ever Since I Met Lucy"	
30948	"Jerri Lee"/"Hey Now"	

End

The Platters

HISTORY AND SOUND

The Platters experienced the meteoric rise to fame every member of every vocal group seeks. Before their unprecedented popularity they had achieved little success with Federal and King Records. The group experimented with the ballad style while with Federal, and "Tell the World" and the original "Only You" were fine ballads, but failed to attract sales. Uptempo songs, such as "My Name Ain't Annie" with Linda Hayes or "Maggie Doesn't Work Here Anymore," also met with little success. Somehow, the label change to Mercury proved magical. The group clicked with a redone "Only You," and from that point their success is legendary. The Platters' string of hits ran throughout the 50's, most notably with "The Great Pretender," "My Prayer," "Twilight Time" and "Smoke Gets in Your Eyes."

RARITY AND VALUE

The Federal/King issues attract collectors' interest. The rarest is "Only You," worth over $50; "Tell the World" brings just under $20. The bulk of the Federal/King records, being jump vocals, are worth under $15. The Mercury releases generally bring under $5. Reissues of the best-selling Mercury releases remain available.

DISCOGRAPHY

Federal

12153	"Give Thanks"/"Hey Now"	1953
12164	"I Need You All the Time"/"I'll Cry When You're Gone"	1954
12181	"Roses of Picardy"/"Beer Barrel Boogie"	
12188	"Tell the World"/"Love All Night"	
12198	"Voo Vee Ah Bee"/"Shake It up Mambo"	
12204	"Maggie Doesn't Work Here Anymore"/"Take Me Back, Take Me Back"	
12244	"Only You"/"You Made Me Cry"	1955
12250	"I Need You All the Time"/"Tell the World"	
12271	"Give Thanks"/"I Need You All the Time"	

King

| 4752 | "My Name Ain't Annie"/"Let's Babalu" (with Linda Hayes) | |
| 4773 | "Please Have Mercy"/"Oochi Pachi" | |

Mercury

70633	"Only You"/"Bark, Battle and Ball"	
70753	"The Great Pretender"/"I'm Just a Dancing Partner"	1956
70819	"The Magic Touch"/"Winner Take All"	
70893	"My Prayer"/"Heaven on Earth"	
70948	"You'll Never Never Know"/"It Isn't Right"	
71011	"One in a Million"/"On My Word of Honor"	
71032	"I'm Sorry"/"He's Mine"	1957
71093	"My Dream"/"I Wanna"	
71184	"Only Because"/"The Mystery of You"	
71246	"Helpless"/"Indiff'rent"	

71289	"Twilight Time"/"Out of My Mind"	1958
71320	"You're Making a Mistake"/"My Old Flame"	
71353	"I Wish"/"It's Raining Outside"	
71383	"Smoke Gets in Your Eyes"/"No Matter What You Are"	
71427	"Enchanted"/"The Sound and the Fury"	1959
71467	"Remember When"/"Love of a Lifetime"	
71502	"Wish It Were Me"/"Where"	
71538	"My Secret"/"What Does It Matter"	
71563	"Harbor Lights"/"Sleepy Lagoon"	

The Spaniels

HISTORY AND SOUND

The Spaniels were a versatile group, performing such sweet romantic ballads as "Goodnight Sweetheart Goodnight," and the deadpan, comic blues "Play It Cool." The group's first Vee Jay release, "Baby It's You," was leased by the fledgling Chicago label to the established Chance label, for whom the record received the bulk of its sales. It was with the later "Goodnight Sweetheart Goodnight" that the Spaniels and Vee Jay Records scored their first smash hit. Later Spaniels records were mainly performed in a ballad style and were consistent sellers.

RARITY AND VALUE

Several of the Spaniels' releases are rare. "Baby It's You" on the Vee Jay label is extremely rare, bringing over $100 on red vinyl. Follow-up releases bring around $10 to $15, while "Dear Heart" and "Since I Fell for You," being poor-sellers, now are worth over $20.

DISCOGRAPHY

Vee Jay

101	"Baby It's You"/"Bounce"	1953
	(also on Chance 1141)	
103	"The Bells Ring Out"/"House Cleaning"	
107	"Goodnight Sweetheart Goodnight"/"You Don't Move Me"	1954
116	"Play It Cool"/"Let's Make Up"	
131	"Do Wah"/"Doncha Go"	
154	"Painted Picture"/"Hey Sister Lizzie"	1955
178	"Do You Really"/"False Love"	
189	"Dear Heart"/"Why Don't You Dance"	
202	"Since I Fell for You"/"Baby Come along with Me"	1956
229	"Please Don't Tease"/"You Gave Me Peace of Mind"	
246	"IOU"/"Everyone's Laughing"	1957
257	"I Need Your Kisses"/"You're Gonna Cry"	
264	"I Lost You"/"Crazee Baby"	
278	"Tina"/"Great Googley Moo"	1958
290	"Stormy Weather"/"Here Is Why I Love You"	
301	"Heart and Soul"/"Baby It's You"	
310	"I Like It Like That"/"Trees"	
328	"100 Years from Today"/"These Three Words"	1959
342	"People Will Say We're in Love"/"The Bells Ring Out"	
350	"I Know"/"Bus Fare Home"	

The Dells

HISTORY AND SOUND

Originally called the El Rays, the group recorded an excellent but poor-selling Checker release. "Tell the World" on Vee Jay sold even fewer copies; however, "Dreams of Contentment" was a hit. "Oh What a Nite" was not only a hit, it was a consistently selling 50's classic. The Dells performed intricately harmonious love ballads with a unique "cool" sound.

RARITY AND VALUE

"Darling I Know" by the El Rays brings around $40; however, "Tell the World" (one of the first records to be bootlegged) brings a more rarefied $100. "Dreams of Contentment" is valued at around $20, while later releases bring up to $10.

DISCOGRAPHY

As by the El Rays:
Checker
794	"Darling I Know"/"Christine"	1953

As by the Dells:
Vee Jay
134	"Tell the World"/"Blues at Three"	1955
166	"Dreams of Contentment"/"Zing Zing Zing"	
204	"Oh What a Nite"/"Jo Jo"	1956
230	"Movin' On"/"I Wanna Go Home"	
236	"Why Do You Have to Go"/"Dance, Dance, Dance"	
251	"A Distant Love"/"O Bop She Bop"	1957
258	"Pain in My Heart"/"Time Makes You Change"	
274	"What You Say Baby"/"The Springer"	

292   "Jeepers Creepers"/"I'm Calling"   1958
300   "Wedding Day"/"My Best Girl"
324   "Dry Your Eyes"/"Baby Open up Your Heart"   1959
338   "Oh What a Nite"/"I Wanna Go Home"

The Flairs

HISTORY AND SOUND

The Flairs in all probability first recorded as the Hollywood Blue Jays. "I Had a Love" was later leased or sold by Hollywood Records to Modern Records and was issued on the subsidiary Flair label. The Flairs had two lead singers—Cornell Gunter on the ballad sides and Richard Berry on the jump sides. The group recorded a limited number of excellent sides—there is not a loser in the lot—but found only limited commercial success. Eventually, the members went separate ways. Richard Berry became successful as a single artist, Cornell Gunter founded the Ermines, and Young Jesse later recorded the hit "Mary Lou" and eventually joined the Coasters.

RARITY AND VALUE

The Hollywood label releases are rare on 78 RPM; their existence on 45 RPM is uncertain, but would certainly be extremely rare. All of the Flair 45's are rare: "You Should Care for Me" and "This Is the Night for Love" are worth over $50; "I Had a Love" and "Getting High," the least rare, bring around $20.

DISCOGRAPHY

As by the Hollywood Blue Jays:
Hollywood
     185   "Cloudy and Raining"/"So Worried"   1951
     396   "I Had a Love"/"Tell Me You're Mine"   1952

As by the Flairs:

Flair

1012	"I Had a Love"/"She Wants to Rock"	1953
1019	"You Should Care for Me"/"Tell Me You Love Me"	1954
1028	"Getting High"/"Love Me Girl"	
1041	"Baby Wants"/"You Were Untrue"	
1044	"This Is the Night for Love"/"Let's Make with Some Love"	
1056	"Hold Me, Thrill Me, Chill Me"/"I'll Never Let You Go"	1955
1067	"My Darling, My Sweet"/"She Loves to Dance"	

The Cadillacs

HISTORY AND SOUND

The Cadillacs' early releases were slow ballads. "Gloria" is a classic, yet poor-selling, record which was re-recorded by several other vocal groups of the era. It's simply a great song. However, the group found commercial success only with the upbeat "Speedo," a major hit. "Speedo" set the pace for the Cadillacs' later releases, all jump novelty-type records.

RARITY AND VALUE

"Wishing Well" and "Gloria," both love ballads, bring over $20. Except for the good-selling "Speedo," which generally brings only $2 or $3, the next few follow-up recordings are priced over $5.

DISCOGRAPHY

Josie

765	"Gloria"/"I Wonder Why"	1954
769	"Wishing Well"/"I Want to Know about Love"	
773	"No Chance"/"Sympathy"	1955
778	"Down the Road"/"Widow Lady"	
785	"Speedo"/"Let Me Explain"	
792	"Zoom"/"You Are"	1956
798	"Betty My Love"/"Woe Is Me"	
805	"The Girl I Love"/"That's All I Need"	
807	"Shock-A-Doo"/"Rudolph the Red-Nosed Reindeer"	
812	"Sugar, Sugar"/"About That Gal Named Lou"	1957
820	"My Girl Friend"/"Broken Heart"	
821	"Lucy"/"Hurry Home"	
829	"Buzz, Buzz, Buzz"/"Yea Yea Baby"	1958
836	"Speedo Is Back"/"A Looka Here"	
842	"I Want to Know"/"Holy Smoke Baby"	
846	"Peek-A-Boo"/"Oh Oh Lolita"	
857	"Jay Walker"/"Copy Cat"	1959
861	"Cool It Fool"/"Please Mr. Johnson"	
866	"Romeo"/"Always My Darling"	
870	"Bad Dan McGoon"/"Dumbell"	

The El Dorados

HISTORY AND SOUND

The El Dorados were a successful Vee Jay group, second only to the Spaniels in sales. The group's first release was the ballad "Baby I Need You." However, in a familiar pattern, the group only scored with the faster-tempo "At My Front Door." The follow-up release, "I'll Be Forever Loving You," another jump song, also provided the group with major chart action. An earlier release, "Annie's Answer," gave the female lead a forum to deny that "Annie" had a baby.

RARITY AND VALUE

On red vinyl, "Baby I Need You" can bring over $40. "Annie's Answer" and "One More Chance" are valued at around $20, while "At My Front Door" brings less than $5.

DISCOGRAPHY

Vee Jay

115	"Baby I Need You"/"My Loving Baby"	1954
118	"Annie's Answer"/"Living with Vivian" (with Hazel McCollum)	
127	"One More Chance"/"Little Miss Love"	1955
147	"At My Front Door"/"What's Buggin' You Baby"	
165	"I'll Be Forever Loving You"/"I Began to Realize"	
180	"Now That You've Gone"/"Rock 'n' Roll's for Me"	
197	"A Fallen Tear"/"Chop Ling Soon"	1956
211	"Bim Bam Boom"/"There in the Night"	
250	"Tears on My Pillow"/"A Rose for My Darling"	1957
263	"Three Reasons Why"/"Boom Diddle Boom"	
302	"Lights Are Low"/"Oh What a Girl"	1958

The Jewels

HISTORY AND SOUND

The Jewels had one very influential record—the original version of "Hearts of Stone." This first release was covered by several other rhythm and blues groups, including the Charms. Follow-up releases included such fine ballads as "A Fool in Paradise" and "Please Return." Other releases included the inferior "Hearts Can Be Broken," an attempt to re-create the success of "Hearts of Stone."

RARITY AND VALUE

"A Fool in Paradise" and "Rosalie" can bring up to $20. Other releases on Imperial and RPM are worth less than $10.

DISCOGRAPHY

R & B

1301	"Hearts of Stone"/"Runnin' "	1954
1303	"A Fool in Paradise"/"Oh Yes I Know"	
1306	"Rosalie"/"Living from Day to Day"	

Imperial

5351	"Hearts Can Be Broken"/"Angel in My Life"	1955
5362	"Please Return"/"Natural, Natural Ditty"	
5377	"How"/"Rickety Rock"	1956
5387	"My Baby"/"Goin', Goin', Gone"	

RPM

474	"She's a Flirt"/"B Bomb Baby"	

The Spiders

HISTORY AND SOUND

The Spiders featured a very unusual blues vocal style. "You're the One" is a classic downtempo group blues ballad. "I'm Slippin' In" and "The Real Thing" are rockers, complete with sexual lyrics; "21" is an excellent rocker with a driving piano. "Witchcraft," a best-seller, is a rolling-tempo love song.

RARITY AND VALUE

Records by the Spiders, being bluesier than other group records, do not command high prices. Thus the rarest releases, "Tears Began to Flow" and "21," bring less than $10.

DISCOGRAPHY

Imperial

5265	"You're the One"/"I Didn't Want to Do It"	1954
5280	"Tears Began to Flow"/"I'll Stop Crying"	
5291	"I'm Slippin' In"/"I'm Searching"	
5305	"Mmm Mmm Baby"/"The Real Thing"	
5318	"21"/"She Keeps Me Wondering"	
5331	"That's Enough"/"Lost and Bewildered"	1955
5344	"Am I the One"/"Sukey, Sukey, Sukey"	
5354	"For a Thrill"/"Bells in My Heart"	
5366	"Witchcraft"/"Is It True"	
5376	"Don't Pity Me"/"How I Feel"	1956
5393	"A-1 in My Heart"/"Dear Mary"	
5405	"That's the Way to Win My Heart"/"Goodbye"	
5423	"Honey Bee"/"That's My Desire"	1957

The Meadowlarks

HISTORY AND SOUND

The Meadowlarks were a West Coast vocal group that recorded for two major rhythm and blues labels. The RPM releases were upbeat, driving records with little commercial action. The first Dootone release, "Heaven and Paradise," provided the group with a best-selling romantic classic. So popular was this ballad style that the group, led by Don Julian, repeated with several other soft ballads. Instead of being repetitious, these releases were individually fine love songs. Don Julian also found success in the 60's with a group named the Larks and a dance called "The Jerk"—or was it the other way around?

RARITY AND VALUE

The RPM releases are rare—"Real Pretty Mama" is worth over $20, "LSMFT Blues" is worth at least $30. The early Dootone releases generally bring in the area of $10 to $12. Most of the big-selling Dootone releases remain available on the reissue Dooto label.

DISCOGRAPHY

RPM
399	"Real Pretty Mama"/"Love Only You"	1954
406	"LSMFT Blues"/"Pass the Gin"	

Dootone
359	"Heaven and Paradise"/"Embarrassing Moments"	1955
367	"Always and Always"/"I Got Tore Up"	
372	"This Must Be Paradise"/"Mine All Mine"	

392   "Please Love a Fool"/"Oop Boopy Oop"   1956
405   "I Am a Believer"/"Boogie Woogie Teenager"
424   "Blue Moon"/"Big Mama Wants to Rock"

The Penguins

HISTORY AND SOUND

The Penguins were the first and most successful Dootone rhythm and blues vocal group. Their first record met with little success, but their second recording, written by Jesse Belvin, was the definitive rhythm and blues hit of the decade. "Earth Angel" was the record, and the song not only provided success for the Penguins, but was also the most consistently selling rhythm and blues record throughout the 50's, and sells well to this day, although the present Dooto reissue has been altered with over-dubbed vibes. Later Penguins releases on Dootone were fine love songs. The group went to Mercury, where they recorded such excellent releases as "Walking Down Broadway" and "A Christmas Prayer."

RARITY AND VALUE

The Penguins' first record, "No There Ain't No News Today," is rare, worth over $30. All of the early Dootone and Mercury issues bring around $10.

DISCOGRAPHY

Dootone
345   "No There Ain't No News Today"/"When
       I'm Gone"   1954

348	"Earth Angel"/"Hey Senorita"	1955
353	"Love Will Make Your Mind Go Wild"/ "Ookey Ook"	
362	"Kiss a Fool Goodbye"/"Baby Let's Make Love"	
428	"I Need You"/"Be My Lovin' Baby"	1956
432	"Sweet Love"/"Your Mind"	1957
435	"Do Not Pretend"/"If You're Mine"	1958
456	"You're An Angel"/"Mr. Junkman"	

Wing

| 90076 | "Dealer of Dreams"/"Peace of Mind" | 1955 |

Mercury

70610	"Be Mine or Be a Fool"/"Don't Do It"	1955
70654	"Walking Down Broadway"/"It Only Happens with You"	
70703	"Devil That I See"/"Promises, Promises, Promises"	
70762	"A Christmas Prayer"/"Jingle Jangle"	
70799	"My Troubles Are Not at an End"/"She's Gone, Gone"	1956
70943	"Earth Angel"/"Ice"	
71033	"Will You Be Mine"/"Cool Baby Cool"	

Atlantic

| 1132 | "Pledge of Love"/"I Knew I'd Fall in Love" | 1957 |

The Medallions

HISTORY AND SOUND

The Medallions, with Vernon Green as lead singer, were the third successful Dootone vocal group. All of the group's releases were romantic ballads, backed with very original jump-tempo songs, often about cars. The harmony and unusual vocal gimmicks used in these fast records make them classic upbeat re-

cordings. The slower ballads, such as "The Letter," are excellent. The Medallions were fine in both styles. Incidentally,
"Buick '59," a 1954 release, was so titled in hopes of becoming
popular again in 1959. No problem: the record sold well through
1959 and for years afterward.

RARITY AND VALUE

Most of the early records bring about $10. Some of the bigger
hits are now issued on Dooto.

DISCOGRAPHY

Dootone

347	"The Letter"/"Buick '59"	1954
357	"The Telegram"/"Coupe de Ville Baby"	1955
364	"Edna"/"Speeding"	
373	"My Pretty Baby"/"I'll Never Love Again"	
379	"Dear Darling"/"Don't Shoot"	
393	"I Want a Love"/"Dance and Swing"	1956
400	"Shedding Tears for You"/"Pushbutton Automobile" (as by Vernon Green)	
407	"Did You Have Fun"/"My Mary Lou"	
419	"For Better or for Worse"/"I Wonder, I Wonder, I Wonder"	
425	"Lover's Prayer"/"Unseen"	
446	"Magic Mountain"/"'59 Volvo"	1957
454	"Behind the Door"/"Rocket Ship"	1958

The Heartbeats

HISTORY AND SOUND

The Heartbeats recorded a dynamite ballad with their widely known "A Thousand Miles Away." The three preceding Hull releases were excellent mellow ballads, but it was the haunting James Sheppard vocal in "A Thousand Miles Away" that created a renowned 50's classic—one of the great records of the era. Follow-up releases by the Heartbeats did not match the greatness of the Hull releases. In 1962, James Sheppard answered his own "A Thousand Miles Away" in Shep and the Limelites' "Daddy's Home," on the reactivated Hull label.

RARITY AND VALUE

The Hull label releases are worth around $20. The Rama releases sell for less than $10, the Gee and Roulette label issues are commonly found and bring less than $5.

DISCOGRAPHY

Hull

711	"Crazy for You"/"Rock 'n' Roll 'n' Rhythm 'n' Blues"		1955
713	"Darling How Long"/"Hurry Home Baby" (also on Gee 1062)		
716	"People Are Talking"/"You Way" (also on Gee 1061)		
720	"A Thousand Miles Away"/"Oh Baby Don't" (also on Rama 216)		1956

Rama

222	"Wedding Bells"/"I Won't Be a Fool Anymore"

231   "Everybody's Somebody's Fool"/"I Want
       to Know"   1957

Network
    200   "Tormented"/"After Everybody's Gone"

Gee
    1043   "When I Found You"/"Hands Off Baby"
    1047   "After New Year's Eve"/"500 Miles to Go"   1958

Roulette
    4054   "Down on My Knees"/"I Found a Job"
    4091   "One Day Next Year"/"Sometimes I Wonder"
    4194   "Down on My Knees"/"Crazy for You"

The Five Satins

HISTORY AND SOUND

The group originally recorded as the Scarlets, issuing some fine sophisticated ballads, particularly "Dear One," later covered by the Ravens. However, the second release by the group (as the Five Satins), the legendary "In the Still of the Night," is considered by many the most successful and significant 50's rhythm and blues record—a monster hit. Follow-up releases were also good-sellers. The Five Satins developed a successful ballad style —Fred Parris' lead vocals with a strong background group— in such records as "Wonderful Girl" and "To the Aisle."

RARITY AND VALUE

The rarest and most valuable records are those by the Scarlets. "Dear One" is worth around $15, the other Red Robin releases are valued slightly higher. The two Five Satins releases on Standord are worth slightly under $10; the Ember label issues bring less than $5.

DISCOGRAPHY

As by the Scarlets:
Red Robin
    128   "Dear One"/"I've Lost"   1954
    133   "Love Doll"/"Darling I'm Yours"
    135   "True Love"/"Cry Baby"   1955
    138   "Kiss Me"/"Indian Fever"
As by the Five Satins:
Standord
    105   "All Mine"/"Rosemarie"
    106   "In the Still of the Night"/"The Jones Girl"   1956
            (also on Ember 1005)
Ember
    1008   "Wonderful Girl"/"Weeping Willow"   1956
    1014   "Oh Happy Day"/"Our Love Is Forever"
    1019   "To the Aisle"/"Wish I Had My Baby"   1957
    1025   "Our Anniversary"/"Pretty Girl"
    1028   "A Million to One"/"Love with No Love in Return"
    1038   "A Night to Remember"/"Senorita Lolita"   1958
    1056   "Shadows"/"Toni My Love"
    1061   "I'll Be Seeing You"/"A Night Like This"   1959
    1066   "Candlelight"/"The Time"
    1070   "Wishing Ring"/"Tell Me Dear"
As by the Scarlets:
Klik
    7905   "She's Gone (With the Wind)"/"The Voice"   1958

Arthur Lee Maye and the Crowns

HISTORY AND SOUND

Arthur Lee Maye is another single artist who recorded some great vocal group records, with his group the Crowns. His records on Modern and RPM are excellent love ballads. "Truly" is in the style of the Moonglows' "Sincerely." Maye's records on Johnny Otis' Dig label were his best recordings and prove that Maye was a master of the slow love song.

RARITY AND VALUE

The rarest Arthur Lee Maye release is "Set My Heart Free," worth over $50. The three releases on RPM can bring from $20 to $30, the Dig releases around $20. All of the records are in great demand. The Specialty release is worth about $10.

DISCOGRAPHY

Modern
	944	"Set My Heart Free"/"I Wanna Love"	1955
RPM			
	424	"Truly"/"Oochie Pachie"	
	429	"Love Me Always"/"Oop De Oop De Oop"	
	438	"Please Don't Leave Me"/"Do the Bop"	
Specialty			
	573	"Gloria"/"Ooh Rooba Lee"	1956
Dig			
	124	"This Is the Nite for Love"/"Honey, Honey"	
	133	"A Fool's Prayer"/"Whispering Winds"	

Cash

    1063   "Honey, Honey"/"Will You Be Mine"
    1065   "All I Want Is Someone to Love"/"Pounding"

Flip

    330   "Cause You're Mine Alone"/"Hey Pretty Girl" 1957

The Cadets / The Jacks

HISTORY AND SOUND

The Cadets and the Jacks were the same group. Recording for the Modern/RPM labels, they appeared as the Cadets on the jump sides, as the Jacks on the slower ballads. The group was proficient at both styles, having a giant hit with each. The Cadets scored with the rock and roll smash, "Stranded in the Jungle" (originally by the Jayhawks), and the Jacks clicked with the plaintive "Why Don't You Write Me" (originally by the Feathers).

RARITY AND VALUE

None of the recordings by the Cadets/Jacks is very rare. The early efforts by the Cadets can bring up to $10, later releases are worth under $5.

DISCOGRAPHY

As by the Cadets:
Modern

    956   "Don't Be Angry"/"I Cry"   1955
    960   "Rollin' Stone"/"Fine Lookin' Baby"
    963   "Fine Lookin' Baby"/"I Cry"

969	"Annie Met Henry"/"So Will I"	1956
971	"Do You Wanna Rock"/"If It Is Wrong"	
985	"Church Bells May Ring"/"Heartbreak Hotel"	
994	"Stranded in the Jungle"/"I Want You"	
1000	"I Got Loaded"/"Dancin' Dan"	
1006	"I'll Be Spinning"/"Fools Rush In"	
1012	"Love Bandit"/"Heaven Help Me"	1957
1017	"You Belong to Me"/"Heaven Help Me"	
1019	"Pretty Evey"/"Run Jamaica Run"	
1024	"Love Can Do Most Everything"/"Hands Across the Table"	
1026	"Ring Chimes"/"Baby Ya Know"	

As by the Jacks:

RPM

428	"Why Don't You Write Me"/"Smack Dab in the Middle"	1955
433	"I'm Confessin' "/"Ever Since My Baby's Been Gone"	
444	"This Empty Heart"/"My Clumsy Heart"	
454	"How Soon"/"So Wrong"	
458	"Sugar Babe"/"Why Did I Fall in Love"	1956
467	"Dream a Little Longer"/"Let's Make Up"	

NOTABLE VOCAL GROUPS

Other exceptional rhythm and blues groups influenced the music during the 50's. Such groups are detailed below in chronological order.

1951–1953

HISTORY AND SOUND

Several early vocal groups performed in a slow, sweet ballad style. These romantic groups included the Larks, the Diamonds, the Velvets and the Five Sharps. "My Reverie" by the Larks, "A Beggar for Your Kisses" by the Diamonds and "I" by the Velvets are good examples of this early mellow style.

The Embers and the Rocketeers each recorded one issue for Herald Records. "Paradise Hill" by the Embers is a pleasing ballad, later to be redone by several rhythm and blues groups. "Foolish One" by the Rocketeers is a stilted, yet effective performance by the group.

A drastic change in vocal style is evident in the Five Willows' recordings. The group recorded three sweetly simple love ballads in 1953. "Dolores," in particular, is a beautiful record. However, they did not have a hit until 1956, with "Church Bells May Ring," a typical rock and roll performance of the period.

The Hawks were an early West Coast group, specializing in a very aggressive and primitive jump sound.

RARITY AND VALUE

The rarest records are several of the Larks' issues—"My Reverie" and "In My Lonely Room" can bring $100. No record by the Larks is valued under $25. The releases by the Diamonds, the Embers, the Rocketeers and the Velvets bring prices ranging from $10 to $20. Early releases by the Five Willows on Allen and Pee Dee are $50, while the extremely rare "White Cliffs of Dover" is easily worth $100. The Herald issues bring close to $20, later releases are worth under $10, except for the original Melba 102—the original was entitled "Church Bells Are Ringing"; later editions of Melba 102 were entitled "Church Bells May Ring"—which is worth over $20. The Hawks' releases bring around $20. Of course, the rarest release is "Stormy Weather" by the Five Sharps, a steal at $100.

DISCOGRAPHY

The Larks:
Apollo

427	"Eyesight to the Blind"	1951
429	"Little Side Car"	
1180	"Hopefully Yours"	
1184	"My Reverie"	
1190	"In My Lonely Room"	1952
1194	"Hold Me"	

The Diamonds:
Atlantic

981	"A Beggar for Your Kisses"	1952
1003	"Two Loves Have I"	1953
1017	"Romance in the Dark"	

The Five Sharps:
Jubilee
    5104   "Stormy Weather"   1952
The Embers:
Herald
    410   "Paradise Hill"   1953
The Hawks:
Imperial
    5266   "Joe the Grinder"   1953
    5306   "Give It Up"   1954
    5317   "All Women Are the Same"
Post
    2004   "These Blues"
The Rocketeers:
Herald
    415   "Foolish One"   1953
The Velvets:
Red Robin
    120   "They Tried"   1953
    122   "I"   1954
    127   "I Cried"
The Five Willows:
Allen
    1000   "My Dear Dearest Darling"   1953
    1002   "Dolores"
    1003   "White Cliffs of Dover"
Pee Dee
    290   "Love Bells"
Herald
    433   "Lay Your Head on My Shoulder"   1954
    442   "Look Me in the Eyes"
Club
    1014   "This Is the End"   1956
Melba
    102   "Church Bells May Ring"
    106   "My Angel"

El Dorado
    508   "The First Taste of Love"   1957
Gone
    5015   "Let's Fall in Love"

1954

HISTORY AND SOUND

Lee Andrews and the Hearts recorded the beautiful "Maybe You'll Be There" in 1954. Three years later the group, in much the same style, recorded two very successful ballad hits, "Long Lonely Nights" and "Teardrops."

One of the biggest rhythm and blues hits was the original recording of "Sh Boom" by the Chords—a record often erroneously associated with the beginning of rock and roll. A similar sophisticated ballad style is evident in the Solitaires' recordings. The group scored with "The Wedding" and "Walking Along" (a major cover hit for the Diamonds on Mercury—no relation to the Atlantic group). The Feathers were a fine West Coast ballad group, issuing several excellent recordings, including the original "Why Don't You Write Me." The Sharptones' single hit release was a beautiful rendition of the standard "Since I Fell for You."

The Diablos were an early Fortune Records (of Detroit) vocal group. "The Wind" is an aggressively performed ballad by lead singer Nolan Strong.

Several good jump groups had hits in 1954. The Bees scored with the very funny off-color "Toy Bell." The Thrillers recorded two excellent records—"The Drunkard" and "Lizabeth," one of the more solid upbeat records released during the period.

An early female group, Shirley Gunter and the Queens, performed the fine classic "Oop Shoop." Etta James, a Johnny Otis discovery, first hit with the "Annie" takeoff, "The Wallflower," with Richard Berry and the Peaches, another early female group. Follow-up releases were great, steady rocking records with a strong gospel-tinged Etta James lead.

The Turbans did very well with the rhythmic "When You Dance" and several later releases. The Toppers' only hit was the double-entendre "Let Me Bang Your Box." The Wrens were a more sophisticated jump group, performing in the early rock and roll style innovated by the Crows in 1953.

The Counts, an early Southern group, specialized in strong, rolling ballads, especially the good-seller "Darling Dear."

RARITY AND VALUE

The rarest releases from 1954 can bring from $75 to $100— notably: "White Cliffs of Dover" by Lee Andrews and the Hearts, "Lonely" by the Solitaires, "C'Est La Vie" by the Wrens, "Dear One" by the Feathers and "Get Away Baby" by the Bees. In the area of $50 are "Since I Fell for You" by the Sharptones, "The Drunkard" and "Lizabeth" by the Thrillers, "Come Back My Love" by the Wrens and "I Don't Stand a Ghost of a Chance" by the Solitaires. "Johnny Darling" and "Love Only You" by the Feathers, "Toy Bell" by the Bees and "Maybe You'll Be There" by Lee Andrews and the Hearts are valued from $20 to $30. Releases by the Diablos, the Toppers, Etta James and the Peaches, the Queens, the Counts, the Turbans and the Chords generally bring around $10.

DISCOGRAPHY

Lee Andrews and the Hearts:
Rainbow

250	"White Cliffs of Dover"	1954
252	"Maybe You'll Be There"	

Gotham

7318	"Bluebird of Happiness"	1955
7321	"Just Suppose"	

Mainline
    102   "Long Lonely Nights"   1957
              (also on Chess 1665)
    105   "Teardrops"
              (also on Chess 1675)
Casino
    110   "Baby Come Back"   1959
  The Bees:
Imperial
    5314   "Toy Bell"   1954
    5320   "Get Away Baby"
  The Chords:
Cat
    104   "Sh Boom"   1954
    109   "Zippity Zum"
    112   "A Girl to Love"
  The Counts:
Dot
    1188   "Darling Dear"   1954
    1199   "Baby Don't You Know"
    1210   "My Dear, My Darling"
    1226   "Baby I Want You"   1955
    1235   "Let Me Go Lover"
    1243   "From This Day On"
    1265   "I Need You Tonight"
    1275   "To Our Love"
  The Diablos:
Fortune
    509   "Adios My Desert Love"   1954
    511   "The Wind"
    514   "Hold Me Until Eternity"   1955
    516   "Daddy Rocking Strong"
    518   "The Way You Dog Me"
    519   "You're the Only Girl, Dolores"
    522   "Teardrops from Heaven"   1956
    525   "Can't We Talk It Over"

The Feathers:
Hollywood
    1051   "Dear One"   1954
Showtime
    1104   "Johnny Darling"
    1105   "Why Don't You Write Me"
    1106   "Love Only You"
Aladdin
    3267   "Johnny Darling"   1955
    3277   "I Need a Girl"
    Etta James and the Peaches:
Modern
    947   "The Wallflower"   1954
    957   "Hey Henry"   1955
    962   "Good Rockin' Daddy"
    972   "W-O-M-A-N"   1956
    984   "Number One"
    988   "Tears of Joy"
    998   "Tough Lover"
    1016   "The Pick-Up"   1957
    1022   "Come What May"
    The Queens:
Flair
    1050   "Oop Shoop"   1954
    The Solitaires:
Old Town
    1000   "Wonder Why"   1954
    1006   "Please Remember My Heart"
    1008   "Lonely"
    1010   "I Don't Stand a Ghost of a Chance"
    1012   "My Dear"
    1014   "The Wedding"   1955
    1015   "Magic Rose"
    1019   "The Honeymoon"
    1026   "The Angels Sang"   1956
    1032   "Give Me One More Chance"

        1034   "Walking Along"   1957
                (also on Argo 5316)
        1044   "I Really Love You So"
        1049   "Walkin' and Talkin' "
    The Sharptones:
Post
        2009   "Since I Fell for You"   1954
    The Thrillers:
Big Town
        109   "The Drunkard"   1954
Herald
        432   "Lizabeth"
    The Toppers:
Jubilee
        5136   "Let Me Bang Your Box"   1954
    The Turbans:
Money
        209   "No No Cherry"   1954
Herald
        458   "When You Dance"   1955
        469   "Sister Sookie"
        478   "I'm Nobody's"   1956
        486   "It Was a Nite Like This"
        495   "Valley of Love"
        510   "Wadda Do"   1957
    The Wrens:
Rama
        53   "Beggin' for Love"   1954
        65   "Come Back My Love"
        174   "Serenade of the Bells"   1955
        175   "Betty Jean"
        184   "I Won't Come to Your Wedding"
        194   "C'Est La Vie"   1956

1955

HISTORY AND SOUND

Several notable ballad groups recorded in the early, relatively unsophisticated style during this transitional year. The Capris, a male group with a female lead, issued several classic recordings, particularly the effective "God Only Knows." The Rivileers recorded several sweetly sung ballads, "A Thousand Stars" (a 1961 hit for Kathy Young and the Innocents), "Eternal Love" and "Sentimental Reasons." The Nutmegs had a major hit with "Story Untold," a mellow ballad sung in a unique, simple style. The Hearts recorded some medium-tempo love ballads, particularly the popular "Lonely Nights."

West Coast groups also recorded in a distinctive fashion. The Chimes, with a Tony Allen lead, performed the consistently selling "Nite Owl," complete with a hooting background member. The Colts' hit record was "Adorable," a ballad with a pop flavor. The Dootones' solitary release was a fine, good-selling ballad, "Teller of Fortune." The Pearls recorded both the upbeat "Real Humdinger," as well as the mellower "Tree in a Meadow," both with a distinctive lead vocal. Donald Woods and the Bel-Aires' "This Paradise" is an emotionally rendered love song, predating the very popular, highly charged "Death of an Angel."

Clyde McPhatter, lately of the Dominoes and established with the Drifters, scored well as a ballad singer. His style approached a middle-of-the-road pop sound with his two hits, "Treasure of Love" and "Without Love." However, McPhatter's "Long Lonely Nights" and "Seven Days" reflect his rhythm and blues roots.

Two Detroit groups specialized in jump vocals. The Five Dollars' "So Strange" and the Don Juans' "Baby I Love You So" were imitated by other, later vocal groups. The Moonlighters, formed with some Moonglows personnel, specialized in upbeat vocals such as "Shoo Doo Be Doo."

West Coast groups recorded some memorable jump records. The Midnights' single release was the answer record "Annie Pulled a Hum-Bug." The Four Deuces did well with "WPLJ" and "Down It Went," both strong drink-oriented vocals. The Dodgers were a pure, unpolished rhythm group, most successful with "Let's Make a Whole Lot of Love."

The year 1955 proved significant as it was at this point that the rock and roll style first achieved widespread success and gained a firm foothold. The Cleftones, the first Gee label rock and roll group, did fairly well with "You, Baby, You," but scored impressively with "Little Girl of Mine." Most notable, however, was the first Teenagers' smash recording, "Why Do Fools Fall in Love." The first major hit in the new idiom featured the thirteen-year-old voice of Frankie Lymon. The Teenagers issued numerous successful rock and roll recordings during the next several years. The Valentines also managed to record successful rock and roll versions of "Lily Maebelle" and "Woo Woo Train."

RARITY AND VALUE

Several releases, including the Four Deuces' "WPLJ" and "Down It Went," the Midnights' release, "Drip Drop" by the Dodgers, "Eternal Love" by the Rivileers, "Real Humdinger" by the Pearls and "God Only Knows" by the Capris, bring from $20 to $30. In the $10 to $20 range are other releases by the Capris, the Pearls on Onyx, "Let's Make a Whole Lot of Love" by the Dodgers, the first two releases by Donald Woods and the Bel-Aires and the single Dootones release. The bulk of the records are worth less than $10, including "Why Do Fools Fall in Love" by the Teenagers and "Treasure of Love" by Clyde McPhatter, both best-sellers and now commonly available. Still available from Fortune Records are most releases by the Five Dollars and the Don Juans.

DISCOGRAPHY

The Capris:
Gotham
    7304   "God Only Knows"   1955
    7306   "It Was Moonglow"
    7308   "It's a Miracle"
20th Century
    1201   "My Weakness"   1956
  The Chimes:
Specialty
    555   "Tears on My Pillow"   1955
    560   "Nite Owl"
    570   "Especially"   1956
    574   "Pretty Little Girl"
  The Cleftones:
Gee
    1000   "You, Baby, You"   1955
    1011   "Little Girl of Mine"   1956
    1016   "Can't We Be Sweethearts"
    1025   "String around My Heart"
    1031   "Why Do You Do Me Like You Do"   1957
    1038   "See You Next Year"
    1041   "Hey Babe"
    1048   "Lover Boy"   1958
  The Colts:
Vita
    112   "Adorable"   1955
    121   "Sweet Sixteen"   1956
    130   "Never No More"
  The Four Deuces:
Music City
    790   "WPLJ"   1955
    796   "Down It Went"   1956

The Dodgers:
Aladdin
 3259 "Let's Make a Whole Lot of Love" 1955
 3271 "Drip Drop"
The Five Dollars:
Fortune
 821 "Doctor Baby" 1955
 826 "So Strange"
 830 "Hard-Working Mama"
 833 "You Fool"
 845 "My Mama Said"
 854 "That's the Way It Goes"
The Don Juans:
Fortune
 825 "Baby I Love You So" 1955
 828 "It's All Over"
 831 "I'm on My Merry Way"
 832 "Baby Child"
 836 "This Is a Miracle"
The Dootones:
Dootone
 366 "Teller of Fortune" 1955
The Hearts:
Baton
 208 "Lonely Nights" 1955
 211 "All My Love Belongs to You"
 222 "Goin' Home to Stay"
 228 "She Drives Me Crazy"
Clyde McPhatter and Vocal Group:
Atlantic
 1070 "Everyone's Laughing" 1955
 1077 "Love Has Joined Us Together"
   (with Ruth Brown)
 1081 "Seven Days"
 1092 "Treasure of Love" 1956

1106	"Thirty Days"	
1117	"Without Love"	
1133	"Just to Hold My Hand"	1957
1149	"Long Lonely Nights"	
1158	"Rock and Cry"	
1170	"No Love Like Her Love"	1958
1185	"Come What May"	
1199	"A Lover's Question"	
2018	"Lovey Dovey"	1959
2028	"Since You've Been Gone"	

The Midnights:

Music City

| 746 | "Annie Pulled a Hum-Bug" | 1955 |

The Moonlighters:

Checker

| 806 | "Shoo Doo Be Doo" | 1955 |
| 813 | "Hug and a Kiss" | |

The Nutmegs:

Herald

452	"Story Untold"	1955
459	"Ship of Love"	
466	"Whispering Sorrows"	
475	"Keys to the Kingdom"	1956
492	"Comin' Home"	
538	"My Sweet Dream"	1957

The Pearls:

Aladdin

| 3265 | "Real Humdinger" | 1955 |

Atco

| 6057 | "Shadows of Love" | 1956 |
| 6066 | "Bells of Love" | |

Onyx

503	"Let's You and I Go Steady"	
506	"Tree in the Meadow"	
510	"I Sure Need You"	1957

511	"Ice Cream Baby"	
516	"It's Love, Love, Love"	

The Rivileers:

Baton

200	"A Thousand Stars"	1955
201	"Forever"	
205	"Eternal Love"	
207	"For Sentimental Reasons"	
209	"Don't Ever Leave Me"	

The Teenagers:

Gee

1002	"Why Do Fools Fall in Love"	1955
1012	"I Want You to Be My Girl"	1956
1018	"I Promise to Remember"	
1022	"The ABC's of Love"	
1026	"I'm Not a Juvenile Delinquent"	
1032	"Teenage Love"	1957
1036	"Out in the Cold Again"	
1039	"Goody Goody"	

The Valentines:

Rama

171	"Lily Maebelle"	1955
181	"I Love You Darling"	
186	"A Christmas Prayer"	
196	"Woo Woo Train"	1956
228	"Don't Say Goodnight"	

Donald Woods and the Bel-Aires:

Flip

303	"This Paradise"	1955
304	"White Port Lemon Juice"	
306	"Death of an Angel"	
309	"Stay with Me Always"	

1956

Several ballad groups adopted a pronounced and aggressive slow rock-and-roll–influenced beat, replacing the early softer sounds. The Channels were an early rock and roll ballad group. "The Closer You Are" and "That's My Desire" featured a strong multilevel vocal performance with a heavy beat. The Mello Kings, the first white group to do well in the rhythm and blues idiom, scored well with the strongly rendered ballad "Tonite, Tonite." The Rays' first release was a simple jump tune, "Moo Goo Gai Pan," rendered in the style of the Five Keys' "Ling Ting Tong," but with less effective lyrics. The first major hit by the Rays was the unusual "Silhouettes," a group recording with strong instrumental backing. The Sensations, another male group with a female lead, performed love ballads. The group's hit, the often recorded "Yes Sir, That's My Baby," is rendered in a slow, halting style. The group also scored in the 60's as the Elgins, with "Darling Baby," sung not much differently from the style of the Sensations.

Several groups recorded in a purer, early rhythm and blues style. The Leaders recorded the classic "Stormy Weather" in a mellow style with a fine lead vocal performance. The Jaguars, a West Coast group, did well with "The Way You Look To-night," an effective and good-selling version of the standard. Little Julian Herrera and the Tigers were popular West Coast entertainers. The group's few recordings reflect a very primitive ballad style. The Youngsters' only hit is a mild 50's classic— "Dreamy Eyes."

Two West Coast groups continued to record in an unsophis-ticated upbeat mode. The Jayhawks' first release was a ballad, "Counting My Teardrops." However, the group's first hit was the original, unpolished version of "Stranded in the Jungle," later a rock and roll hit for the Cadets. The Jivers never had a major hit, although the group recorded two good jump records, "Cherie" and "Ray Pearl."

The Gladiolas, a Southern group, did well with "Little Darlin' " (later covered by the Diamonds on Mercury—a million-seller) and "Shoop Shoop"—both with strong and loud instrumental backing.

Andre Williams, backed by the Don Juans vocal group, sang in a droll, deadpan style. His hit recordings were the "Bacon Fat" dance and the offbeat "Jail Bait."

James Brown, today the foremost soul singer, clicked with his first release, the sobbing "Please, Please, Please," performed with the Famous Flames vocal group. The next major smash, "Try Me," also featured a strong, pleading James Brown vocal.

Rock and roll continued to be the preferred vocal group style. Two Josie label groups scored in 1956. The Chips issued one record, "Rubber Biscuit," a rock and roll novelty with intriguing nonsense lyrics. The Emanons' sole release, the rocking "Blue Moon," was a huge 1961 hit for the Marcels, who performed it in much the same style as the original. The Dell Vikings, an early integrated group, first recorded the ballad "Over the Rainbow." However, the rock and roll releases, "Come Go with Me" and "Whispering Bells," were the major hit records for the group. Using ingenious harmonies, Kripps Johnson, the Dell Vikings' lead singer, developed a unique style evident in the later release "I'm Spinning." The G Clefs recorded a highly sophisticated rock and roll hit, "Ka Ding Dong." The Magnificents had one rock and roll hit, "Up on the Mountain," and several ballads, most notable of which was the poor-selling "Ozetta."

The Six Teens and the Teen Queens were two early female vocal groups. Trudy Williams, the lead vocalist of the Six Teens, effectively rendered the plaintive "A Casual Look" and "Only Jim," both good-sellers. "Eddie My Love" by the Teen Queens was a dry, medium-tempo love ballad.

RARITY AND VALUE

Recordings by Little Julian Herrera on Dig, the Leaders and the Jivers bring about $20. Recordings by the Dell Vikings on Fee Bee, the Channels on Whirlin' Disc, the Chips, the Jaguars and the first Jayhawks release bring from $10 to $15. Other recordings issued in 1956 generally are valued at less than $10. "Ka Ding Dong" by the G Clefs, "Please, Please, Please" by James Brown and "Up on the Mountain" by the Magnificents were good-sellers and are now commonly available.

DISCOGRAPHY

James Brown and the Famous Flames:
Federal

12258	"Please, Please, Please"	1956
12277	"Hold My Baby's Hand"	
12289	"Just Won't Do Right"	
12290	"I Won't Plead No More"	
12292	"Gonna Try"	1957
12295	"Messing with the Blues"	
12300	"I Walked Alone"	
12311	"That Dood It"	
12316	"Begging, Begging"	1958
12337	"Try Me"	
12348	"I Want You So Bad"	
12352	"I've Got to Change"	

The Channels:
Whirlin' Disc

100	"The Closer You Are"	1956
102	"The Gleam in Your Eyes"	
107	"I Really Love You"	1957
109	"Flames in My Heart"	

Gone
    5012   "That's My Desire"   1958
    5019   "Altar of Love"
Fury
    1021   "My Love Will Never Die"
  The Chips:
Josie
    803   "Rubber Biscuit"   1956
  The Dell Vikings:
Luniverse
    106   "Over the Rainbow"   1956
Fee Bee
    205   "Come Go with Me"
            (also on Dot 15538)
    210   "Uh Uh Baby"
    214   "Whispering Bells"
            (also on Dot 15592)
Dot
    15571   "What Made Maggie Run"   1957
    15636   "I'm Spinning"
  The Emanons:
Josie
    801   "Blue Moon"   1956
  The G Clefs:
Pilgrim
    715   "Ka Ding Dong"   1956
  The Gladiolas:
Excello
    2101   "Little Darlin' "   1956
    2136   "Shoop Shoop"
  Little Julian Herrera and the Tigers:
Dig
    118   "Lonely, Lonely Nights"   1956
    137   "Symbol of Heaven"

Starla

      6   "I Remember Linda"   1957

  The Jaguars:

Aardell

    0003   "I Wanted You"   1956

    0006   "You Won't Believe Me"

R-Dell

    11   "The Way You Look Tonight"

Original Sound

    06   "Thinking of You"   1959

  The Jivers:

Aladdin

    3329   "Cherie"   1956

    3347   "Ray Pearl"

  The Jayhawks:

Flash

    104   "Counting My Teardrops"   1956

    109   "Stranded in the Jungle"

    111   "Love Train"

  The Leaders:

Glory

    235   "Stormy Weather"   1956

    239   "Dearest Beloved Darling"

    243   "Can't Help Lovin' That Girl"

  The Mello Kings:

Herald

    502   "Tonite, Tonite"   1956

    507   "Chapel on the Hill"

    511   "Baby Tell Me"   1957

    518   "Valarie"

    536   "Chip Chip"

  The Magnificents:

Vee Jay

    183   "Up on the Mountain"   1956

    208   "Caddy Bo"

235   "Off the Mountain"   1957
281   "Ozetta"   1958
The Rays:
Chess
1613   "Moo Goo Gai Pan"   1956
1678   "How Long Must I Wait"   1957
Cameo
117   "Silhouettes"
The Sensations:
Atco
6056   "Yes Sir, That's My Baby"   1956
6067   "Please Mr. Disc Jockey"
6075   "My Heart Cries for You"
6083   "Little Wallflower"
The Six Teens:
Flip
315   "A Casual Look"   1956
317   "Afar into the Night"
320   "Only Jim"   1957
322   "Arrow of Love"
326   "Baby You're Dynamite"
The Teen Queens:
RPM
453   "Eddie My Love"   1956
Andre Williams and the Don Juans:
Fortune
824   "Going down to Tia Juana"   1956
831   "Bacon Fat"
834   "You Are My Sunshine"
837   "Jail Bait"
839   "The Greasy Chicken"
The Youngsters:
Empire
109   "Dreamy Eyes"   1956

1957

HISTORY AND SOUND

In 1957, the rock and roll ballad form reached its greatest popularity. Many groups adopted this style, several with only a single successful release.

The Dubs were an excellent ballad group—the strong beat and emotional power of "Could This Be Magic" and "Chapel of Dreams" are undeniable. The Charts' "Deserie" is a unique blend of voices in a compelling performance. The Jesters, Paragons and Collegians all had fine, solid-selling hits for the Winley label. The Jesters scored with "The Wind" (originally by the Diablos) and "So Strange" (a Five Dollars original). The Paragons recorded two pounding ballads, "Florence" and "Let's Start All Over Again." The Collegians' hit was the classic rock and roll "Zoom, Zoom, Zoom." The Jive Bombers recorded "Bad Boy," a lazily sung, offbeat record. The Shells did well with the harmonious "Baby Oh Baby," a long-time consistent seller. "Six Months, Three Weeks" by the Sharps featured a strong lead and good vocal backing. The Tune Weavers' smash record was the ironic "Happy, Happy Birthday Baby." The Enchanters scored with two excellent releases, both mild hits. "True Love Gone" is an excellent ballad, while "There Goes (A Pretty Girl)" is a fine upbeat effort.

Several West Coast groups saw chart action. The Cuff Links recorded the classic ballads "Guided Missiles" and "Lawful Wedding." "Glory of Love" and "Melody of Love" by the Velvetones feature a dominant narration by the spurned lead. Both recordings were quite popular. Bobby Day and the Satellites recorded the original version of the rock and roll hit "Little Bitty Pretty One," and followed through with the extremely popular "Rockin' Robin."

Several female vocal groups recorded best-sellers. "The Plea" by the Chantels was a hit. However, the group was most successful in later releases, including "Maybe" and "I Love You So," both performed in a stirring, gospel-rooted style. The

Bobbettes, best known for "Mr. Lee," recorded several repeat rock and roll novelties. Their "You Are My Sweetheart" is an excellent love ballad. The Silhouettes' "Get a Job" was a smash uncompromising rock and roll hit. Later releases were also fine rockers and good sellers.

RARITY AND VALUE

The most valuable releases from 1957 are the Velvetones' two recordings and the original "Six Months, Three Weeks" by the Sharps, both worth from $15 to $20. Other releases by the Dubs, the Enchanters, the Silhouettes and the Cuff Links can bring slightly under $10. Several of the major hits from the year remain available, including most of the Winley label issues.

DISCOGRAPHY

The Bobbettes:
Atlantic

1144	"Mr. Lee"	1957
1159	"Speedy"	
1187	"Zoomy"	1958
1194	"The Dream"	
2027	"You Are My Sweetheart"	

The Chantels:
End

1001	"The Plea"	1957
1005	"Maybe"	
1015	"Every Night"	1958
1020	"I Love You So"	
1026	"Prayee"	
1030	"Congratulations"	
1037	"Never Let Me Go"	
1048	"I'm Confessin'"	1959

The Charts:
Everlast
    5001   "Deserie"   1957
    5002   "Dance Girl"
  The Collegians:
Winley
    224   "Zoom, Zoom, Zoom"   1957
  The Cuff Links:
Dootone
    409   "Guided Missiles"
    413   "How You Lied"
    414   "Off-Day Blues"
    422   "It's Too Late Now"
    433   "So Tough"   1958
    434   "A Fool's Fortune"
    438   "Lawful Wedding"
  The Dubs:
Gone
    5002   "Don't Ask Me (To Be Lonely)"   1957
    5011   "Could This Be Magic"
    5020   "Beside My Love"   1958
    5034   "Be Sure My Love"
               (also on Mark X 8008)
    5046   "Chapel of Dreams"
               (also on Gone 5069)
  The Enchanters:
Coral
    61756   "True Love Gone"   1957
    61832   "There Goes"
  The Jesters:
Winley
    218   "So Strange"   1957
    225   "The Plea"
    242   "The Wind"

The Jive Bombers:
Savoy
    1508   "Bad Boy"   1957
  The Paragons:
Winley
    215   "Florence"   1957
    220   "Let's Start All Over Again"
  The Sharps:
Tag
    2200   "Six Months, Three Weeks"   1957
            (also on Chess 1690)
  The Shells:
Johnson
    104   "Baby Oh Baby"   1957
    109   "Better Forget Him"
    110   "In the Dim Light of the Dark"   1958
    119   "Deep in My Heart"
    120   "A Toast to Your Birthday"
  Bobby Day and the Satellites:
Class
    211   "Little Bitty Pretty One"   1957
    220   "Sweet Little Thing"   1958
    229   "Rockin' Robin"
  The Silhouettes:
Junior
    396   "I Sold My Heart to the Junkman"   1957
            (also on Ace 552)
Ember
    1029   "Get a Job"
    1032   "Headin' for the Poorhouse"   1958
    1037   "Bing Bong"
  The Tune Weavers:
Casa Grande
    4037   "Happy, Happy Birthday Baby"   1957
            (also on Checker 872)

3038	"My Congratulations Baby"	
4038	"I Remember Dear"	1958
101	"Little Boy"	

The Velvetones:

Aladdin

3372	"Glory of Love"	1957
3391	"Melody of Love"	

1958

HISTORY AND SOUND

During 1958, a few outstanding group recordings were issued. The Danleers recorded the fine medium-tempo "One Summer Night." The Shields released a best-seller, "You Cheated"—one of the better, driving ballads of the year. Jerry Butler and the Impressions, both major 60's performers, first recorded the silky-smooth ballad "For Your Precious Love." The Miracles, now the premier Motown group, first recorded in a rock and roll style. "Bad Girl" is a beautiful ballad with a strong "Smokey" Robinson lead.

Several rock and roll groups produced important hits in 1958. The Monotones, a hard-driving rock and roll group, scored well with "Book of Love." The Olympics established a wild uptempo style with "Western Movies" and "Big Boy Pete"—both classic rock and roll performances.

The Capris, a white rhythm and blues group, recorded the strolling ballad, "There's a Moon Out Tonight." The record was a real sleeper, not becoming a hit until 1961. The Elegants, another white group, hit with the sophisticated "Little Star." Dion and the Belmonts were a third white group. Influenced by both rock and roll and rhythm and blues, they recorded "I Wonder Why," pure rock and roll; "No One Knows," an appealing ballad; and "A Teenager in Love," a major hit performed in the pop style favored by later vocal groups.

RARITY AND VALUE

The rarest releases from 1958 are the original "For Your Precious Love" by Jerry Butler and "Book of Love" by the Monotones, both worth about $10. The bulk of the releases are worth under $5, for example, "Little Star" by the Elegants and "Western Movies" by the Olympics, now widely available.

DISCOGRAPHY

Jerry Butler and the Impressions:
Falcon

1013	"For Your Precious Love"	1958
	(also on Abner 1013)	

The Capris:
Planet

1010	"There's a Moon Out Tonight"	1958
	(also on Old Town 1094)	

The Danleers:
AMP

1005	"One Summer Night"	1958
	(also on Mercury 71322)	

Dion and the Belmonts:
Laurie

3013	"I Wonder Why"	1958
3015	"No One Knows"	
3027	"A Teenager in Love"	1959
3035	"Lover's Prayer"	
3044	"That's My Desire"	

The Elegants:
Apt

25005	"Little Star"	1958

The Miracles:
End

1016	"My Mama Told Me"	1958
1029	"Money"	
	(also on End 1084)	

Chess

1734	"Bad Girl"	1959
1768	"All I Want"	

The Monotones:
Mascot

124	"Book of Love"	1958
	(also on Argo 5290)	
5301	"Zombi"	
5321	"Legend of Sleepy Hollow"	
5339	"Tell It to the Judge"	

The Olympics:
Demon

1508	"Western Movies"	1958
1512	"Dance with the Teacher"	

Arvee

562	"Hully Gully"	1959
595	"Big Boy Pete"	

The Shields:
Tender

507	"You Cheated"	1958
	(also on Dot 15808)	
518	"I'm Sorry Now"	
	(also on Dot 15856)	
521	"Play the Game Fair"	

1959

HISTORY AND SOUND

In 1959, the classic rhythm and blues style began to diminish in favor of the milder and more commercial soul sound.

Two major rock and roll hits were "Rama Lama Ding Dong," an aggressive performance by the Edsels, and "So Fine," a fine jump version of the Johnny Otis original by the Fiestas. The Falcons' "You're So Fine" featured the strong gospel-influenced lead of Wilson Pickett with heavy vocal and instrumental backing.

The Skyliners, a white group, effectively merged rhythm and blues with a pop sound in recording two excellent ballads— "Since I Don't Have You" and "This I Swear."

RARITY AND VALUE

The only record worth over $5 is the original issue of "You're So Fine" by the Falcons.

DISCOGRAPHY

The Edsels:
Twin
700   "Rama Lama Ding Dong"   1959
The Falcons:
Flick
001   "You're So Fine"   1959
(also on Unart 2013)
The Fiestas:
Old Town
1062   "So Fine"   1959

The Skyliners:
Calico

| 103 | "Since I Don't Have You" | 1959 |
| 106 | "This I Swear" | |

RHYTHM AND BLUES DUETS

The rhythm and blues duet complemented the success of the vocal group. Many of the romantic and upbeat duet performances were similar to vocal group renditions. However, greater expression on the part of the individual duet vocalist was possible. Behind the lead singer, group members were often submerged in the overall sound—often just singing "do-wop, do-wop." Duet members were able to establish an individual presence.

Duets were either formed by two male members or by a male-female combination. The latter paring allowed a unique exchange of dialogue—an effective method of communicating a love song.

The two most successful duets were Marvin and Johnny, and Shirley and Lee.

Shirley and Lee

HISTORY AND SOUND

Shirley Goodman and Leonard Lee, "The Sweethearts of the Blues," were the most popular 50's duet. Their first record, "I'm Gone," is a medium-tempo love ballad with a New Orleans boogie piano. Several follow-up releases, such as "Shirley Come Back to Me," "Shirley's Back" and "The Proposal," trace the ups and downs of a courtship between the pair. "Feel So Good" was their first rock and roll release, but they became a national sensation with the incomparable rocker "Let the Good Times Roll"—the best "party" record of the decade.

RARITY AND VALUE

The first Shirley and Lee release, "I'm Gone," is rare and can bring over $20. The next five Aladdin label releases are worth about $10. Later releases were big sellers and bring less than $5.

DISCOGRAPHY

Aladdin

3153	"I'm Gone"/"Sweethearts"	1952
3175	"Shirley Come Back to Me"/"Baby"	1953
3192	"Shirley's Back"/"So in Love"	
3205	"The Proposal"/"Two Happy People"	
3222	"Lee Goofed"/"Why Did I"	1954
3244	"Confessing"/"Keep On"	
3258	"Comin' Over"/"Takes Money"	1955
3289	"Feel So Good"/"You'll Be Thinking of Me"	
3302	"I'll Do It"/"Lee's Dream"	
3313	"That's What I'll Do"/"A Little Word"	1956
3325	"Let the Good Times Roll"/"Do You Mean to Hurt Me"	
3338	"I Feel Good"/"Now That It's Over"	
3362	"When I Saw You"/"That's What I Wanna Do"	1957
3369	"I Want To Dance"/"Marry Me"	
3380	"Rock All Nite"/"Don't You Know I Love You"	
3390	"Rockin' with the Clock"/"The Flirt"	
3405	"I'll Thrill You"/"Love No One but You"	

3418   "Don't Leave Me Here to Cry"/"Everyone's
         Rockin' "   1958
3432   "All I Want to Do Is Cry"/"Come on and
         Have Your Fun"
3455   "When Day Is Done"/"True Love"

Marvin and Johnny

HISTORY AND SOUND

Marvin and Johnny formed after the dissolution of the Jesse
Belvin and Marvin Phillips duet—after only one release. The
early Specialty recordings of Marvin and Johnny are slow, sweet
harmonies. The first Modern label release was "Cherry Pie," a
50's classic and long-time best-seller. Although no other Marvin
and Johnny records sold quite as well, the style of the duet
never varied from the beautiful sound of that record.

RARITY AND VALUE

The Specialty releases bring about $5, the Modern records from
$2 to $5.

DISCOGRAPHY

Specialty
479   "Baby Doll"/"I'm Not a Fool"   1953
488   "Jo Jo"/"How Long Has She Been Gone"
498   "School of Love"/"Boy Loves Girl"
530   "Day in, Day Out"/"Flip"
554   "Ding Dong Daddy"/"Mambo"   1954

Modern

	933	"Cherry Pie"/"Tick Tock"	
	941	"Kiss Me"/"Sugar"	
	946	"Honey Girl"/"Little Honey"	
	949	"Ko Ko Mo"/"Sometimes I Wonder"	1955
	952	"I Love You, Yes I Do"/"Baby Won't You Marry Me"	
	959	"Sugar Mama"/"Butter Ball"	
	968	"Sweet Dreams"/"Will You Love Me"	1956
	974	"Ain't That Right"/"Let Me Know"	

Aladdin

	3335	"My Dear, My Darling"/"Hey Chicken"	
	3371	"Pretty Eyes"/"Yak Yak"	1957
	3408	"You're in My Heart"/"Smack Smack"	

Kent

	303	"Cherry Pie"/"Ain't That Right"	1958

NOTABLE DUETS

Several duets recorded some great hits during the 50's. Gene
and Eunice scored with the original version of the rocking "Ko
Ko Mo" and "This Is My Story," a beautiful, mellow ballad.
Johnnie and Joe, a male-female duo, clicked with the 1957
classic, "Over the Mountain, Across the Sea," an eerie, slow
rocker. Mickey and Sylvia's "Love Is Strange" and Robert and
Johnny's "We Belong Together" were both very distinctive
medium-tempo love ballads. Don and Dewey, although never
scoring a major hit, were a great rock and roll duet, in the
Specialty Records tradition. "Justine" and "Ko Ko Joe" are
wild screaming rockers, "When the Sun Begins to Shine" and
"Leavin' It All Up to You" are slow bluesy rolling piano vocals.

RARITY AND VALUE

None of these recordings is rare. Those in demand by collectors
are the very early Mickey and Sylvia and Robert and Johnny
issues, which generally bring prices in the $5 area.

DISCOGRAPHY

Gene and Eunice:
Combo
| | 64 | "Ko Ko Mo" | | 1955 |
Aladdin
| | 3276 | "Ko Ko Mo" |
| | 3282 | "This Is My Story" |

3292	"Flim Flam"	1956
3305	"I Gotta Go Home"	
3315	"Hootchy Kootchy"	
3321	"Let's Get Together"	
3351	"Bom Bom Lulu"	
3374	"The Vow"	1957
3376	"Doodle Doodle Doo"	
3414	"I Mean Love"	1958

Case

1001	"Poco Loco"	1958
1002	"You Think I'm Not Thinking"	
1007	"Sugar Babe"	

Mickey and Sylvia:

Rainbow

316	"I'm So Glad"	1955
318	"Rise Sally Rise"	
330	"Where Is My Honey"	

Groove

0164	"No Good Lover"	1956
0175	"Love Is Strange"	

Vik

0267	"There Oughta Be a Law"	1957
0280	"Love Will Make You Fail in School"	
0290	"Love Is a Treasure"	
0297	"Where Is My Honey"	

Robert and Johnny:

Old Town

1021	"Train to Paradise"	1955
1029	"You're Mine"	1956
1038	"Don't Do It"	1957
1043	"Broken-Hearted Man"	
1047	"We Belong Together"	1958
1052	"Marry Me"	
1068	"Dream Girl"	1959
1072	"Bad Dan"	

Johnnie and Joe:

J&S

	1631	"Warm, Soft and Lovely"	1956
	1641	"I'll Be Spinning" (also on Chess 1641)	
	1654	"Over the Mountain, Across the Sea" (also on Chess 1654)	1957
	1659	"It Was There"	

Chess

	1677	"I Was So Lonely"	
	1693	"Why Did She Go"	
	1706	"Darling"	1958

Gone

| | 5024 | "Who Do You Love" | |

Don and Dewey:

Specialty

	599	"Jungle Hop"	1957
	610	"Leavin' It All Up to You"	
	617	"When the Sun Has Begun to Shine"	
	631	"Justine"	1958
	639	"Ko Ko Joe"	
	659	"Big Boy Pete"	1959

BLUES AND RHYTHM AND
BLUES VOCALISTS

Rhythm and blues single vocalists recorded in progressively different styles throughout the 50's:

1. The early rhythm and blues artist can trace his roots to blues music recorded prior to World War II. Towards the 50's, the style of both the city blues singer and the country blues singer were evolving into rhythm and blues. City blues vocalists included Ivory Joe Hunter, Ray Charles and Chuck Willis; and "shouters" such as Bullmoose Jackson, Wynonie Harris and Joe Turner. City blues singers were backed by big bands or unobtrusive accompaniment, usually a piano and guitar. Country blues artists included Muddy Waters, John Lee Hooker, Little Walter, Rufus Thomas and Howlin' Wolf. These bluesmen are often associated with highly charged, primitive guitar and vocal expression. Early recorded efforts of the country blues singers were usually distributed only in "the country"—the Southern states.

2. Rhythm and blues performers drew from both the city and country blues styles. Early recordings of Little Richard and Fats Domino feature some very basic instrumentation, generally piano and guitar, along with "shouting"-type vocals.

3. The rock and roll style was first performed by Joe Turner, whose record "Shake, Rattle and Roll" (later recorded by Bill Haley and the Comets) was a major 1954 rhythm and blues hit.

4. As with group vocal recordings, 1955 was the year the rock and roll style became dominant. Several hit records provided the momentum for the great popularity of the rock and roll approach. "Ain't It a Shame" by Fats Domino, "Tutti Frutti"

by Little Richard and "Maybellene" by Chuck Berry were three major hits of 1955 and were the first best-sellers for each of the vocalists. All three artists continued to record important rock and roll hits throughout the 50's. Later rhythm and blues singers who successfully recorded rock and roll were Huey "Piano" Smith and Larry Williams.

A brief examination of the styles and recordings of each of these artists follows.

Fats Domino

HISTORY AND SOUND

The early recordings by Fats Domino represent a "New Orleans Sound"—his great boogie-blues piano with a driving rhythm. "Goin' Home" and "Going to the River" are slow-rocking gems. "Mardi Gras in New Orleans" and "Little School Girl" are classic boogie-woogie piano workouts with a distinct New Orleans flavor. Fats Domino hit the top-forty threshold in 1955 with "Ain't It a Shame" (successfully covered by Pat Boone), then recorded a string of major hits throughout the remainder of the decade. During this period, his style became somewhat subdued, but the quality of his work never suffered.

RARITY AND VALUE

The rarest Fats Domino releases are his first ten to twelve issues. On 45 RPM each can bring at least $20. Later releases bring $10. Records issued after his big hit, "Ain't It a Shame," were best-sellers and thus are worth only $1 or $2.

DISCOGRAPHY

Imperial

5058	"The Fat Man"/"Detroit City Blues"	1949
5065	"Boogie-Woogie Baby"/"Little Bee"	1950
5077	"Hide Away Blues"/"She's My Baby"	
5085	"Hey La Bas Boogie"/"Brand New Baby"	
5099	"Every Night about This Time"/"Korea Blues"	
5114	"Tired of Crying"/"What's the Matter Baby"	1951
5123	"Don't You Lie to Me"/"Sometimes I Wonder"	
5138	"Right from Wrong"/"No No Baby"	
5145	"Rockin' Chair"/"Careless Love"	
5167	"I'll Be Gone"/"You Know I Miss You"	1952
5180	"Goin' Home"/"Reeling and Rocking"	
5197	"Poor Poor Me"/"Trust in Me"	
5209	"How Long"/"Dreaming"	
5220	"Nobody Loves Me"/"Cheatin' "	1953
5231	"Going to the River"/"Mardi Gras in New Orleans"	
5240	"Please Don't Leave Me"/"The Girl I Love"	1953
5251	"Rose Mary"/"You Said You Love Me"	
5262	"Don't Leave Me This Way"/"Something's Wrong"	
5272	"Little School Girl"/"You Done Me Wrong"	1954
5283	"Baby Please"/"Where Did You Stay"	
5301	"I Lived My Life"/"You Can Pack Your Suitcase"	
5313	"Don't You Hear Me Calling You"/"Love Me"	
5323	"Thinking of You"/"I Know"	1955
5340	"Don't You Know"/"Helping Hand"	
5348	"Ain't It a Shame"/"La La"	
5357	"All by Myself"/"Troubles of My Own"	
5369	"Poor Me"/"I Can't Go On"	
5375	"Bo Weevil"/"Don't Blame It on Me"	1956

5386   "I'm in Love Again"/"My Blue Heaven"
5396   "So Long"/"When My Dreamboat Comes Home"
5407   "Blueberry Hill"/"Honey Chile"
5417   "Blue Monday"/"What's the Reason"
5428   "I'm Walkin' "/"I'm in the Mood for Love"   1957
5442   "Valley of Tears"/"It's You I Love"
5454   "When I See You"/"What Will I Tell My Heart"
5467   "Wait and See"/"I Still Love You"
5477   "I Want You to Know"/"The Big Beat"
5492   "Don't You Know I Love You"/"Yes My
            Darling"   1958
5515   "Sick and Tired"/"No No"
5526   "Little Mary"/"Prisoner's Song"
5537   "Young School Girl"/"It Must Be Love"
5553   "Whole Lotta Lovin' "/"Coquette"
5569   "Telling Lies"/"When the Saints Go
            Marching In"   1959
5585   "I'm Ready"/"Margie"
5606   "I Want to Walk You Home"/"I'm Gonna
            Be a Wheel Someday"
5629   "Be My Guest"/"I've Been Around"

Ray Charles

HISTORY AND SOUND

Ray Charles, in his early career, sang in a style a shade bluesier
than Nat "King" Cole. At first, he performed with several bands
prior to becoming known in his own right. His early pre-Atlantic
recordings reflect a simple "West Coast" feeling—blues vocals
with piano, guitar and drums accompaniment. With Atlantic,
Ray Charles began performing his own compositions, including
the humorous "It Should've Been Me" and the rocking "This

Little Girl of Mine." He hit it big with "I've Got a Woman," but after "What'd I Say," he never looked back. Since leaving Atlantic, Charles has dabbled in pop and country and western styles, but his recent "Feel So Bad" and "What Am I Living For" show he has not abandoned his roots.

RARITY AND VALUE

It is unclear whether the Swingtime releases were all pressed on 45 RPM; however, those on 45 RPM are worth between $10 and $20. The early Atlantic releases are worth just under $10. Releases issued after "I've Got a Woman" bring from $2 to $5.

DISCOGRAPHY

Downbeat
171	"Confession Blues"/"I Love You, I Love You"	1949
178	"Blues Before Sunrise"/"How Long Blues"	

Swingtime
215	"I've Had My Fun"/"Sittin' on Top of the World"	
217	"See See Rider"/"What Have I Done"	
218	"Honey, Honey"/"She's on the Ball"	
228	"Late in the Evening Blues"/"The Egg Song"	
239	"I'll Do Anything but Work"/"Someday"	1950
249	"All to Myself"/"I Wonder Who's Kissing Her Now"	
250	"Baby Let Me Hold Your Hand"/"Lonely Boy"	1951
274	"Kiss-A-Me Baby"/"I'm Glad for Your Sake"	
297	"Hey Now"/"Baby Won't You Please Come Home"	
300	"Guitar Blues"	
326	"Misery in My Heart"/"The Snow Is Falling"	1952

Sittin' In With

641   "Guitar Blues"/"Baby Let Me Hear You
         Call My Name"
651   "I Can't Do No More"/"Roly Poly"

Rockin'

504   "Walkin' and Talkin' to Myself"/"I'm
         Wonderin' and Wonderin' "   1953

Atlantic

976   "Roll with My Baby"/"The Midnight Hour"   1952
984   "Jumpin' in the Mornin' "/"Sun's Gonna
         Shine Again"   1953
999   "Mess Around"/"Funny"
1008   "Feelin' Sad"/"Heartbreaker"
1021   "It Should've Been Me"/"Sinner's Prayer"   1954
1037   "Don't You Know"/"Losing Hand"
1050   "I've Got a Woman"/"Come Back"
1063   "This Little Girl of Mine"/"A Fool for You"   1955
1076   "Greenbacks"/"Blackjack"
1085   "Drown in My Own Tears"/"Mary Ann"   1956
1096   "Hallelujah I Love Her So"/"What Would I
         Do without You"
1108   "Leave My Woman Alone"/"Lonely Avenue"
1124   "Ain't That Love"/"I Want to Know"   1957
1143   "It's All Right"/"Get on the Right Track Baby"
1154   "Swanee River Rock"/"I Want a Little Girl"
1172   "Talking about You"/"What Kind of
         Man Are You"   1958
1180   "Yes Indeed"/"I Had a Dream"
1196   "You Be My Baby"/"My Bonnie"
2006   "Rockhouse Pt. 1 & 2"   1959
2010   "The Right Time"/"Tell All the World
         about You"
2022   "That's Enough"/"Tell Me How Do You Feel"
2031   "What'd I Say Pt. 1 & 2"
2043   "I'm Movin' On"/"I Believe to My Soul"

Ruth Brown

HISTORY AND SOUND

Ruth Brown was the earliest important female rhythm and blues vocalist and the first female singer to record for Atlantic. Several of her earliest releases were performed with the pioneer vocal group, the Delta Rhythm Boys. Ruth Brown's earliest best-sellers were "Teardrops from My Eyes," "5-10-15 Hours" and "Mama He Treats Your Daughter Mean"—each is rendered in Miss Brown's upbeat pleading blues style. She also recorded some sadder blues, including "R.B. Blues" and the powerful "Oh What a Dream." She did not score a smash, top-forty hit until 1957 with the rock and roller "Lucky Lips."

RARITY AND VALUE

The rarest Ruth Brown records are the earliest. The most valuable is "Someday," worth from $15 to $20. Other Ruth Brown releases, including "Teardrops from My Eyes" and "5-10-15 Hours" can bring over $10. Later Ruth Brown releases are worth from $2 to $5.

DISCOGRAPHY

Atlantic

879	"So Long"/"It's Raining"	1949
887	"I'll Get Along Somehow"/"Rocking Blues"	
893	"Happiness Is a Thing Called Joe"/"Love Me Baby"	
899	"Someday"/"Why"	1950
	(with the Delta Rhythm Boys)	
905	"I Can Dream, Can't I"/"Sentimental Journey"	
917	"Dear Little Boy of Mine"/"Where Can I Go"	

919	"Teardrops from My Eyes"/"Am I Making the Same Mistake"	
930	"I'll Wait for You"/"Standing on the Corner"	1951
941	"I Know"/"I Don't Want Anybody at All"	
948	"Without My Love"/"Shine On"	
962	"5-10-15 Hours"/"Be Anything"	1952
973	"Daddy, Daddy"/"Have a Good Time"	
978	"Three Letters"/"Good for Nothing Joe"	1952
986	"Mama, He Treats Your Daughter Mean"/ "R.B. Blues"	1953
993	"Wild Wild Young Men"/"Mend Yours Ways"	
1005	"The Tears Keep Tumbling Down"/"I Would if I Could	
1018	"Love Contest"/"If You Don't Want Me"	
1023	"It's All in Your Mind"/"Sentimental Journey" (with the Delta Rhythm Boys)	1954
1027	"Hello Little Boy"/"Had Any Sense"	
1036	"Oh What a Dream"/"Please Don't Freeze"	
1044	"Somebody Touched Me"/"Mambo Baby"	
1051	"Bye Bye Young Men"/"Ever Since My Baby's Been Gone"	
1059	"As Long as I'm Moving"/"I Can See Everybody's Baby	1955
1072	"It's Love Baby"/"What'd I Say"	
1082	"I Want to Do More"/"Ol' Man River"	
1091	"Sweet Baby of Mine"/"I'm Getting Right"	1956
1102	"I Want to Be Loved"/"Mom Oh Mom"	
1113	"Smooth Operator"/"I Still Love You"	
1125	"Lucky Lips"/"My Heart Is Breaking over You"	1957
1140	"One More Time"/"When I Get You Baby"	
1153	"I Hope We Meet"/"Show Me"	
1166	"Look Me Up"/"A New Love"	1958
1177	"Just Too Much"/"Book of Lies"	
1197	"This Little Girl's Gone Rockin' "/"Why Me"	

2008	"Mama, He Treats Your Daughter Mean"/ "I'll Step Aside"
2015	"5-10-15 Hours"/"Itty Bitty Girl"
2026	"Jack o'Diamonds"/"I Can't Hear a Word You Say"
2035	"I Don't Know"/"Papa Daddy"

Chuck Willis

HISTORY AND SOUND

Chuck Willis' recording career commenced with some very bluesy releases for Columbia and Okeh. This downbeat style was to influence his recordings throughout the 50's. His very first recordings were poor sellers, his only hit was "Caldonia." "Going to the River" was the Fats Domino song rendered in a melancholy vein—a very effective recording. Willis' first national hit was "C. C. Rider" possibly the first "stroll" record. One of his last releases, "What Am I Living For" ironically was issued the year he died. Two other fine Atlantic label records by Chuck Willis are "It's Too Late" and "Thunder and Lightning."

RARITY AND VALUE

The rarest Chuck Willis records are the obscure Columbia and Okeh releases, bringing from $10 to $15. Later Okeh releases are worth $5 to $10, Atlantic issues are in the $2 range.

DISCOGRAPHY

Columbia

39238	"It Ain't Right to Treat Me Wrong"/ "Can't You See"	1950

Okeh

6810	"I Tried"/"I Rule My House"	1951
6841	"Let's Jump Tonight"/"It's Too Late Baby"	
6873	"Here I Come"/"Loud Mouth Lucy"	1952
6905	"Caldonia"/"My Story"	
6930	"Salty Tears"/"Wrong Lake to Catch a Fish"	
6952	"Going to the River"/"Baby Have Left Me Here Again"	1953
6985	"Don't Deceive Me"/"I've Been Treated Wrong Too Long"	
7004	"My Baby Is Coming Home"/"When My Day Is Over"	
7015	"You're Still My Baby"/"What's Your Name"	
7029	"I Feel So Bad"/"Need One More Chance"	1954
7041	"Change My Mind"/"My Heart's Been Broke Again"	
7048	"I've Been Away Too Long"	
7051	"Love Struck"/"Lawdy Miss Mary"	1954
7055	"I Can Tell"/"One More Break"	
7062	"Search My Heart"/"Ring Ding Doo"	1955
7067	"Come On Home"	
7070	"Charged with Cheating"/"Two Spoon of Tears"	1956

Atlantic

1098	"Kansas City Woman"/"It's Too Late"	
1112	"Juanita"/"Whatcha Gonna Do When Your Baby Leaves You"	
1130	"C. C. Rider"/"Ease the Pain"	1957
1148	"Love Me Cherry"/"That Train Has Gone"	
1168	"Betty and Dupree"/"My Crying Eyes"	1958
1179	"What Am I Living For"/"Hang up My Rock and Roll Shoes"	
1192	"Thunder and Lightning"/"My Life"	
2005	"Keep A-Drivin' "/"You'll Be My Love"	
2029	"Just One Kiss"/"My Baby"	1959

Little Richard

HISTORY AND SOUND

Little Richard Penniman is the first to admit that his career is legend. His earliest RCA releases reflect a different Little Richard from the later popular star—a blues boogie-woogie singer with a distinctive youthful voice. His Peacock recordings, featuring Little Richard as a member of the Tempo Toppers vocal group, provide a hint of his developing style. Richard's first Specialty label record was like none other he had previously recorded. The record was the dynamic, pounding rocker, "Tutti Frutti." Immediately successful, "Tutti Frutti" established Little Richard's rock and roll style for the remainder of his 50's career. He recorded "Long Tall Sally," "Rip It Up," "She's Got It," "Lucille" and "Keep A-Knockin'," all wild rockers and dynamite best-sellers. The flip sides of the last two of these releases, "Send Me Some Lovin' " and "Can't Believe You Wanna Leave," were great medium-tempo, piano rockers—a style reminiscent of his Peacock recordings. Little Richard's great Specialty recordings constitute an unparalleled contribution to rock and roll, some of the best examples of this musical form.

RARITY AND VALUE

The RCA recordings are so very scarce that they bring some of the highest prices for single-artist rhythm and blues records, often selling for over $50. The Peacock releases are worth from $5 to $10. The Specialty issues were nonstop sellers and thus bring $1 or $2, at most.

DISCOGRAPHY

RCA

4392   "Every Hour"/"Taxi Blues"   1952

4582	"Get Rich Quick"/"Thinkin' about My Mother"	
4722	"Why Did You Leave Me"/"Ain't Nothing Happenin'"	
5025	"Please Have Mercy on Me"/"I Brought It All on Myself"	

Peacock

1616	"Fool at the Wheel"/"Ain't That Good News"	1952
1628	"Rice, Red Beans and Turnip Greens"/"Always"	1954
1658	"Directly from My Heart"/"Little Richard's Boogie"	1955
1673	"Maybe I'm Right"/"I Love My Baby"	

Specialty

561	"Tutti Frutti"/"I'm Just a Lonely Guy"	1955
572	"Long Tall Sally"/"Slippin' and Slidin'"	1956
579	"Rip It Up"/"Reddy Teddy"	
584	"She's Got It"/"Heebie Jeebies"	
591	"The Girl Can't Help It"/"All Around the World"	
598	"Lucille"/"Send Me Some Lovin'"	1957
606	"Jenny, Jenny"/"Miss Ann"	
611	"Keep A-Knockin'"/"Can't Believe You Wanna Leave"	
624	"Good Golly Miss Molly"/"Hey Hey Hey Hey"	1958
633	"True Fine Mama"/"Ooh My Soul"	
645	"Baby Face"/"I'll Never Let You Go"	
652	"She Knows How to Rock"/"Early One Morning"	1959
660	"By the Light of the Silvery Moon"/"Wonderin'"	
664	"Kansas City"/"Lonesome and Blue"	
670	"Shake a Hand"/"All Night Long"	
680	"Maybe I'm Right"/"Whole Lotta Shakin'"	
681	"I Got It"/"Baby"	
686	"Directly from My Heart"/"Most I Can Offer"	

Lloyd Price

HISTORY AND SOUND

Lloyd Price was the second most successful Specialty label rhythm and blues singer. His first record, "Lawdy Miss Clawdy," was his best seller on Specialty and sold well throughout the decade. Follow-up releases were fine records, generally in the slow piano boogie "Clawdy" style. Others, such as "Tell Me Pretty Baby" and "Country Boy Rock" were fine uptempo records. However, none of these later releases sold well. With the switch to ABC records, Lloyd Price rediscovered a hit formula with the good-seller "Just Because," and two top-forty monsters, "Stagger Lee" and "Personality."

RARITY AND VALUE

No Lloyd Price record is of great rarity. "Lawdy Miss Clawdy" remains available, but is diluted with a dubbed-in chorus. On red plastic, some early Specialty issues go for over $10. Other releases on Specialty and ABC bring $1 or $2.

DISCOGRAPHY

Specialty

428	"Lawdy Miss Clawdy"/"Mailman Blues"	1952
440	"Oooh Oooh Oooh"/"Restless Heart"	
452	"Tell Me, Pretty Baby"/"Ain't It a Shame"	
457	"So Long"/"What's the Matter Now"	1953
463	"Where You At"/"Baby Don't Turn Your Back on Me"	
471	"I Wish Your Picture Was You"/"Frog Legs"	
483	"Let Me Come Home Baby"/"Too Late for Tears"	

494	"Walking the Track"/"Jimmie Lee"	1954
535	"Chee Koo Baby"/"Oo Ee Baby"	
540	"Tryin' to Find Someone to Love"/	
	"Lord Lord Amen"	1955
571	"I Yi Yi Gomen Y Sai"/"Woe Ho Ho"	
578	"Country Boy Rock"/"Rock 'n' Dance"	
582	"Forgive Me Clawdy"/"I'm Glad, Glad"	1956
602	"Breaking My Heart"/"Baby Please Come Home"	

KRC

301	"The Chicken and the Bop"/"Lonely Chair"	1957
303	"Hello Little Girl"/"Georgiana"	
305	"How Many Times"/"To Love and Be Loved"	
5000	"No Limit To Love"/"Such a Mess"	
5002	"Gonna Let You Come Back Home"/	
	"Down By the River"	

ABC

9792	"Just Because"/"Why"	1957
9972	"Stagger Lee"/"You Need Love"	1958
9997	"Where Were You"/"Is It Really Love"	1959
10018	"Personality"/"Have You Ever Had the Blues"	
10032	"I'm Gonna Get Married"/"Three Little Pigs"	

Jimmy Reed

HISTORY AND SOUND

Jimmy Reed is a well-known Chicago blues artist. He is identified with his heavy droning guitar and harmonica sound, represented by his much-copied "Baby What You Want Me to Do" —his one major hit. By the late 50's, Jimmy Reed's records tended to become monotonous, almost formula products. Thus, his earliest recordings, particularly "Little Rain" and the instrumental "Roll and Rhumba," are his most interesting works.

Regardless of the sameness of his later records, however, the toughness and intensity of all his performances cannot be denied.

RARITY AND VALUE

The rarest Jimmy Reed record is his first release, worth over $10 on either Vee Jay or Chance. Later Vee Jay releases bring from $5 to $10, but records released after the hit "Baby What You Want Me to Do" are worth little more than $2.

DISCOGRAPHY

Vee Jay

100	"Roll and Rhumba"/"High and Lonesome"	1953
	(also on Chance 1142)	
105	"Found My Baby"/"Jimmy's Boogie"	
119	"Boogie in the Dark"/"You Don't Have to Go"	1954
132	"I'm Gonna Ruin You"/"Pretty Thing"	
168	"Baby Don't Say That No More"/	
	"Ain't That Lovin' You Baby"	1955
186	"Rockin' with Reed"/"Can't Stand to See You Go"	
203	"My First Plea"/"I Love You Baby"	1956
226	"You've Got Me Dizzy"/"Honey Don't Let Me Go"	
237	"Little Rain"/"Honey, Where You Going"	1957
248	"The Sun Is Shining"/"Baby What's on	
	Your Mind"	
270	"You're Something Else"/"A String to My Heart"	
275	"Go on to School"/"You Got Me Crying"	1958
287	"I Know It's a Sin"/"Down in Virginia"	
298	"I'm Gonna Get My Baby"/"Odds and Ends"	
304	"I Told You Baby"/"Ends and Odds"	
314	"Take Out Some Insurance"/	
	"You Know I Love You"	1959

326   "Going to New York"/"I Wanna Be Loved"
333   "Baby What You Want Me to Do"/
      "Caress Me Baby"
347   "Found Love"/"Where Can You Be"

Johnny Ace

HISTORY AND SOUND

The recording career of Johnny Ace was cut tragically short by Russian roulette on Christmas Day, 1954. His hit record, "Pledging My Love," was released immediately after his death. His loss, felt deeply by his fans, caused "Pledging My Love" to sell well long after its 1955 release. Earlier efforts by Johnny Ace, "Cross My Heart" and "The Clock," were sung in his typically plaintive ballad style.

RARITY AND VALUE

The sole record on the Flair label is rare and now brings over $10. Releases on the Duke label are worth under $5, while "Pledging My Love" remains available, but with additional dubbed-in instrumentation.

DISCOGRAPHY

Flair
    1015   "Midnight Hours Journey"/"Trouble and Me"   1953
Duke
    102   "My Song"/"Follow the Rule"   1952
    107   "Cross My Heart"/"Angel"   1953
    112   "The Clock"/"Ace's Wild"

118	"Saving My Love for You"/"Yes Baby"	1954
128	"Please Forgive Me"/"You've Been Gone So Long"	
132	"Never Let Me Go"/"Burley Cutie"	
136	"Pledging My Love"/"No Money"	1955
144	"Anymore"/"How Can You Be So Mean"	
148	"So Lonely"/"I'm Crazy Baby"	
154	"Still Love You So"/"Don't You Know"	1956

Richard Berry

HISTORY AND SOUND

Richard Berry's recording career began with two poor-selling releases on the Flair label. Berry attracted attention as the lead on the Robins' smash hit, "Riot in Cell Block #9." Flair records had him record the strikingly similar "The Big Break," which although not a hit, established Richard Berry as a major rhythm and blues talent. Several of his later Fair label releases, such as "Oh Oh Get Out of the Car" and "Next Time," were rendered in an ironic, comic style. He also performed some warm, romantic ballads, such as "Please Tell Me" and "Baby Darling." Richard Berry achieved his greatest success with "Louie Louie," a record that became one of the most durable and all-time best-selling rock and roll songs. His follow-up releases were fairly successful, especially the rocker "Have Love, Will Travel."

RARITY AND VALUE

The earliest Flair recordings, especially those sung with a vocal group, bring prices from $15 to $20. The RPM releases are valued in the $5 range, the Flip label records bring $2.

DISCOGRAPHY

Flair

	1016	"I'm Still in Love with You"/"One Little Prayer"	1953
	1052	"Bye Bye"/"At Last" (with the Dreamers)	1954
	1055	"The Big Break"/"What You Do to Me"	1955
	1058	"Baby Darling"/"Daddy-Daddy" (with the Dreamers)	
	1064	"Oh Oh Get Out of the Car"/"Please Tell Me"	
	1068	"Don'cha Go"/"God Gave Me You"	
	1071	"Next Time"/"Crazy Love"	
	1075	"Jelly Roll"/"Together"	

RPM

	448	"Big John"/"Rockin' Man"	1955
	452	"I Am Bewildered"/"Pretty Brown Eyes"	
	465	"Yama Yama Pretty Mama"/"Angel of My Life"	1956
	477	"Good Love"/"Wait for Me"	

Flip

	318	"Take the Key"/"No Kissin' and A-Huggin' "	
	321	"Louie, Louie"/"You Are My Sunshine"	1957
	327	"Sweet Sugar You"/"Rock, Rock, Rock"	
	331	"You're the Girl"/"You Look So Good"	1958
	336	"The Mess Around"/"Heaven on Wheels"	
	339	"Besame Mucho"/"Do I Do I"	
	349	"Have Love, Will Travel"/"No Room"	1959
	352	"I'll Never Love Again"/"Somewhere There's a Rainbow"	
	360	"You Are My Sunshine"/"You Look So Good"	

Bo Diddley

HISTORY AND SOUND

Bo Diddley, a Chicago recording artist, performed in a very distinct and affirmatively upbeat blues style. His first and by far largest hit, "Bo Diddley," is an intriguing combination of a blues-voodoo style with a rock and roll beat. He continued to use this style with later recordings, the ominous "Who Do You Love" and the wild chanter, "Mona" (later recorded by the Rolling Stones). "Bring It to Jerome" is a strange, offbeat rocker, while "She's Fine, She's Mine" uses some wild instrumentation and chanting to produce a bizarre effect. "Say Man," a best-seller, is a series of mutual put-downs between Bo Diddley and his maracas player, Jerome Green.

RARITY AND VALUE

While later best-selling issues rarely go for more than $2, early Bo Diddley releases are worth about $5. "Bo Diddley" is the one exception—being a solid hit, it is now commonly available and is worth about $2.

DISCOGRAPHY

Checker

814	"Bo Diddley"/"I'm a Man"	1955
819	"Diddley Daddy"/"She's Fine, She's Mine"	
827	"Bring It to Jerome"/"Pretty Thing"	
832	"Diddy Wah Diddy"/"I Am Looking for a Woman"	1956
842	"Who Do You Love"/"I'm Bad"	
850	"Down Home Train"/"Cops and Robbers"	

860	"Hey Bo Diddley"/"Mona"	1957
878	"Boss Man"/"Before You Accuse Me"	
896	"Hush Your Mouth"/"Dearest Darling"	1958
907	"Willie and Lillie"/"Bo Meets the Monster"	
917	"I'm Sorry"/"Oh Yea"	
924	"Crackin' Up"/"The Great Grandfather"	1959
931	"Say Man"/"The Clock Strikes Twelve"	
936	"Say Man Back Again"/"She's Alright"	

Chuck Berry

HISTORY AND SOUND

Chuck Berry's first recording was the rock and roll "Maybellene," an instant hit and a consistent seller. His follow-up releases sold well in the rhythm and blues market. His next major hit was "School Days," a dramatic expression of the teenage high-school life style of the 50's. After he received a good deal of exposure on American Bandstand, Chuck Berry had four top-forty releases in 1957–1958—"School Days, Rock and Roll Music" (an early Beatles hit), "Sweet Little Sixteen" and "Johnny B. Goode." After 1958, Berry's career declined; however, he did record the fine "Memphis, Tennessee" (a late 60's hit for Johnny Rivers). Chuck Berry's late 60's comeback resulted in some fine recordings in his rocking 50's style.

RARITY AND VALUE

Chuck Berry's poorest sellers, "Thirty Days" and "No Money Down," are the rarest, worth about $5. Other early releases bring about $2.

DISCOGRAPHY

Chess

1604	"Maybellene"/"Wee Wee Hours"	1955
1610	"Thirty Days"/"Together"	
1615	"No Money Down"/"The Downbound Train"	1956
1626	"Roll Over Beethoven"/	
	"Too Much Monkey Business"	
1645	"You Can't Catch Me"/"Havana Moon"	
1653	"School Days"/"Deep Feeling"	1957
1664	"Oh Baby Doll"/"La Juanda"	
1671	"Rock and Roll Music"/"Blue Feeling"	
1683	"Sweet Little Sixteen"/"Reelin' and	
	Rockin'"	1958
1691	"Johnny B. Goode"/"Around and Around"	
1697	"Beautiful Delilah"/"Vacation Time"	
1700	"Carol"/"Hey Pedro"	
1709	"Sweet Little Rock and Roller"/	
	"Jo Jo Gunne"	
1714	"Merry Christmas Baby"/"Run, Rudolph, Run"	
1716	"Anthony Boy"/"That's My Desire"	1959
1722	"Almost Grown"/"Little Queenie"	
1729	"Memphis, Tennessee"/"Back in the U.S.A."	

NOTABLE BLUES AND RHYTHM
AND BLUES ARTISTS

1947–1950

HISTORY AND SOUND

Country blues singers John Lee Hooker and Lightnin' Hopkins were prolific recording artists whose records were issued by just about every major rhythm and blues label. Hooker recorded under various pseudonyms—Delta John for the Regent label, Texas Slim for King, Birmingham Sam and His Magic Guitar for Savoy, Johnny Williams for Gotham and Swingtime and as John Lee Booker for Chess and Chance. Along with Muddy Waters, Hooker and Hopkins were the most popular of the very early postwar country blues artists. Each had a best-seller: "Boogie Chillen" by John Lee Hooker; "Shotgun Blues" by Lightnin' Hopkins; and "I'm Your Hoochie Coochie Man" by Muddy Waters. Each of the three records were down-home guitar blues recordings.

B. B. King recorded a large number of titles for the RPM label, but did not score a hit until "Everyday I Have the Blues," a rolling blues vocal. Lowell Fulson's "Lonesome Christmas" is a funky down-tempo blues classic; however, "Reconsider Baby" was his first hit.

Little Walter Jacobs recorded a good-seller called "Juke"— a fine guitar and harmonica instrumental in a mellow, low-down blues style. "You're So Fine" and "My Babe" were both uptempo vocal blues hits. Sticks McGhee's "Drinkin' Wine

Spo-Dee-O-Dee" was his only major hit. Rufus Thomas' first release was a downtempo blues; his first hit record was "Bear Cat," patterned on "Hound Dog." His current releases for the Stax label of Memphis are best-sellers.

Several trends started in this early era. King was the first label with hit records containing obvious sexual references. Bullmoose Jackson's "I Want a Bowlegged Woman" and "Sneaky Pete" and Wynonie Harris' "Lovin' Machine" were issued on King. Amos Milburn recorded a number of hits in the early 50's. His "Chicken Shack Boogie" is a great boogie piano rocker, and his records about drinking, "Let Me Go Home Whiskey" and "One Scotch, One Bourbon, One Beer," helped start a major rhythm and blues trend.

Ivory Joe Hunter recorded both piano instrumentals and some fine city blues vocals. His early hit was "I Almost Lost My Mind," a classic blues ballad. Much later, Hunter hit with "Since I Met You Baby," performed in much the same style. Johnny Otis was basically an instrumental performer and band leader, whose records featured vocals by some of his discoveries —the Robins, Mel Williams, Little Esther Phillips, Mel Walker and Arthur Lee Maye. Otis also discovered Etta James and "Big Mama" Thornton. Johnny Otis' biggest hit record was the 1958 release "Willie and the Hand Jive."

Smiley Lewis, an early piano blues performer, recorded the original versions of "Blue Monday" (a later Fats Domino hit) and "One Night" (a 1959 Elvis Presley hit). Lewis' biggest hit was "I Hear You Knockin' " (a cover hit for Gail Storm), a record that influenced Fats Domino's later successful style.

Joe Turner recorded some early city blues, which although rhythm and blues hits, did not sell nearly as well as his later rock and roll records.

RARITY AND VALUE

Not all of these early releases were issued on 45 RPM. The rarest and most valued by collectors are the early country blues releases. These pre-1950 issues by Lightnin' Hopkins, Muddy

Waters, John Lee Hooker and Amos Milburn bring up to $15 on 78 RPM, and well over $20 on 45 RPM. Other first releases by Bullmoose Jackson, Wynonie Harris, Ivory Joe Hunter, Smiley Lewis and Little Walter are worth about $10 on 45 RPM. Releases by other early artists, including B. B. King and Lowell Fulson, bring from $5 to $10.

DISCOGRAPHY

Ivory Joe Hunter:
King

4183	"San Francisco Blues"	1947
4208	"Come On, Let Your Hair Down"	
4220	"Don't Fall in Love with Me"	
4232	"What Did You Do to Me"	1948
4255	"No Money, No Luck Blues"	
4275	"I Don't Know"	
4291	"Waiting in Vain"	
4306	"Guess Who"	
4314	"Jealous Heart"	
4326	"I Quit My Pretty Mama"	1949
4347	"Please Don't Cry Anymore"	
4382	"Changing Blues"	
4405	"Lying Woman"	
4423	"False Friend Blues"	
4443	"She's Gone Blues"	

MGM

10578	"I Almost Lost My Mind"	
10618	"SP Blues"	1950
10663	"I Need You So"	
10733	"Let Me Dream"	
10761	"Living a Lie"	
10818	"It's a Sin"	1951
10861	"Sorta Need You So"	

10899	"I Found My Baby"	
10951	"I Can't Get You off My Mind"	
10995	"When I Lost You"	
11052	"Wrong Woman Blues"	1952
11132	"Blue Moon"	
11165	"Where Shall I Go"	
11195	"I Will Be True"	
11263	"I Get That Lonesome Feeling"	1953
11378	"Rockin' Chair Boogie"	
11459	"If You See My Baby"	
11549	"Don't Make Me Cry"	
11599	"My Best Wishes"	
11818	"Do You Miss Me"	1954

Atlantic

1049	"I Got to Learn to Do the Mambo"	
1066	"Heaven Came Down to Earth"	1955
1086	"A Tear Fell"	
1095	"You Mean Everything to Me"	1956
1111	"Since I Met You Baby"	
1128	"Empty Arms"	
1151	"She's Gone"	1957
1164	"All About the Blues"	
1173	"You're on My Mind"	1958
1183	"I'm So Glad I Found You"	
1191	"Yes I Want You"	

Bullmoose Jackson:

King

4171	"Don't You Think I Ought to Know"	1947
4181	"Sneaky Pete"	
4189	"I Want a Bowlegged Woman"	
4213	"Cleveland, Ohio, Blues"	
4244	"I Know Who Threw the Whiskey in the Well"	1948
4250	"We Can Talk Some Trash"	
4280	"Don't Ask Me Why"	

4288	"Moosey"	
4322	"Why Don't You Haul Off and Love Me"	1949
4535	"All Night Long"	1952
4580	"Big Ten Inch Record"	

Muddy Waters:

Aristocrat

1302	"Little Anna Mae"	1947
1305	"I Can't Be Satisfied"	1948
1307	"Mean Red Spider"	1949
1308	"Train Fare Home"	
1310	"Streamline Woman"	
1311	"Little Geneva"	
406	"Screamin' and Cryin' "	1950
412	"Rollin' and Tumblin' "	

Chess

1426	"Rollin' Stone"	1950
1434	"You're Gonna Need My Help"	
1441	"Louisiana Blues"	
1452	"Long Distance Call"	1951
1468	"Honey Bee"	
1480	"Still a Fool"	
1490	"She Moves Me"	
1509	"Country Boy"	1952
1514	"Please Have Mercy"	
1526	"Standing Around Crying"	
1537	"She's Alright"	1953
1542	"Baby Please Don't Go"	
1550	"Mad Love"	
1560	"I'm Your Hoochie Coochie Man"	
1571	"Just Make Love to Me"	1954
1579	"I'm Ready"	
1585	"I'm a Natural-Born Lover"	1955
1596	"I Want to Be Loved"	
1602	"Manish Boy"	
1612	"Sugar Sweet"	1956
1620	"Forty Days and Forty Nights"	

1630	"Diamonds at Your Feet"	
1644	"Just to Be with You"	1957
1652	"Got My Mojo Working"	
1667	"Good News"	
1680	"Evil"	1958
1692	"She's Got It"	
1704	"She's Nineteen Years Old"	
1718	"Mean Mistreater"	1959
1724	"Clouds in My Heart"	

Wynonie Harris:

King

4210	"Good Rockin' Tonight"	1948
	(also on King 5416)	
4291	"Bloodshot Eyes"	1949
	(also on King 4461)	
4292	"Drinkin' Wine Spo-Dee-O-Dee"	
4485	"Lovin' Machine"	1951

John Lee Hooker:

Modern

627	"Boogie Chillen"	1948
	(also on Modern 893; Kent 332)	
663	"Hoogie Boogie"	
688	"Whistlin' and Moanin' Blues"	1949
714	"Crawlin' Kingsnake"	
730	"Howlin' Wolf"	
746	"No Friend Around"	1950
767	"Roll 'n' Roll"	
790	"Let Your Daddy Ride"	
814	"John L's House Rent Boogie"	1951
829	"Women in My Life"	
835	"I'm in the Mood"	
847	"Turn Over a New Leaf"	1952
862	"Cold Chills All over Me"	
876	"It Hurts Me So"	
886	"Key to the Highway"	
897	"Rock House Boogie"	1953

901	"Ride Til I Die"	
908	"Love Money Can't Buy"	
916	"Too Much Boogie"	
923	"Down Child"	
931	"I Wonder Little Darling"	1954
935	"Let's Talk It Over"	
942	"Bad Boy"	
948	"Shake, Holler and Run"	
958	"Taxi Driver"	1955
966	"The Syndicator"	
978	"I'm Ready"	

Chart

609	"Wobbling Baby"	1955
614	"Blue Monday"	

Vee Jay

188	"Trouble Blues"	1956
205	"Baby Lee"	
233	"I'm Worried Baby"	
245	"I'm So Excited"	1957
255	"Rosie Mae"	
265	"Unfriendly Woman"	
293	"I Love You Honey"	1958
308	"Maudie"	
319	"Boogie Chillen"	
331	"Hobo Blues"	1959
349	"No Shoes"	

B. B. King:

Bullet

309	"Miss Martha King"	1949
311	"Got the Blues"	

RPM

304	"B. B. Boogie"	1950
311	"The Other Night Blues"	1951
318	"My Baby's Gone"	
323	"B. B. Blues"	

330	"She's a Mean Woman"	
339	"Three O'Clock Blues"	1952
348	"She Don't Love Me No More"	
355	"Shake It Up and Go"	
360	"Gotta Find My Baby"	
363	"You Don't Want Me"	1953
374	"Story from My Heart and Soul"	
380	"Woke Up This Morning"	
386	"Highway Bound"	
391	"Neighborhood Affair"	
395	"Why Did You Leave Me"	1954
403	"Praying to the Lord"	
408	"I Love You Baby"	
411	"Everything I Do Is Wrong"	
412	"When My Heart Beats Like a Hammer"	
416	"You Upset Me Baby"	
421	"Everyday I Have the Blues"	
425	"Lonely and Blue"	1955
430	"Shut Your Mouth"	
435	"Talkin' the Blues"	
437	"Ten Long Years"	
450	"Cracking Up over You"	
451	"Crying Won't Help You"	
457	"Let's Do the Boogie"	1956
468	"Sweet Little Angel" .	
479	"On My Word of Honor"	
486	"Early in the Morning"	1957
492	"I Want to Get Married"	
494	"Quit My Baby"	
498	"I Wonder"	
501	"The Key to My Kingdom"	1958

Kent

301	"You Know I Go for You"	
307	"Don't Look Now But You Got the Blues"	
315	"Please Accept My Love"	
330	"Sweet Sixteen"	1959

Sticks McGhee:
Atlantic
    873   "Drinkin' Wine Spo-Dee-O-Dee"   1949

Amos Milburn:
Aladdin
    3014   "Chicken Shack Boogie"   1949
              (also on Aladdin 3332)
    3018   "Bewildered"
    3023   "Jitterbug Baby"   1950
    3026   "Pot Luck Boogie"
    3032   "Roomin' House Boogie"   1950
    3037   "Let's Make Christmas Merry Baby"
    3038   "Real Pretty Mama"
    3043   "I'm Just a Fool in Love"
    3049   "Walkin' Blues"
    3056   "Anybody's Blues"
    3058   "Birmingham Bounce"   1951
    3059   "Hard Luck Blues"
    3060   "Sax Shack Boogie"
              (also on Aladdin 3064)
    3068   "Bad Bad Whiskey"
    3080   "Let's Rock Awhile"
    3090   "Last Mistake—Goodbye"
    3093   "Just One More Drink"
    3105   "She's Gone Again"
    3124   "Thinkin' and Drinkin' "   1952
    3125   "Put Something in My Hand"
    3133   "Roll Mr. Jelly"
    3146   "Everything I Do Is Wrong"
    3150   "Greyhound"
    3159   "Rock, Rock, Rock"
    3164   "Let Me Go Home Whiskey"
    3168   "Long, Long Day"
    3197   "One Scotch, One Bourbon, One Beer"   1953
    3218   "Good, Good Whiskey"

Lightnin' Hopkins:
Aladdin

3005	"Big Mama Jump"	1949
3015	"Sugar Mama"	
3028	"Nightmare Blues"	1950
3035	"Morning Blues"	
3052	"Baby Child"	
3063	"Shotgun Blues"	1951
3077	"Moonrise Blues"	
3096	"Abeline"	
3117	"You're Not Gonna Worry My Life Anymore"	

RPM

337	"Bad Luck and Trouble"	1952
346	"Jake Head Boogie"	
351	"Last Affair"	1953
359	"One Kind Favor"	
378	"Candy Kitchen"	
388	"Mistreater Blues"	1954
398	"Santa Fe Blues"	

Herald

425	"Lightnin's Boogie"	1954
428	"Lightnin's Special"	
436	"Moovin' Out Boogie"	
443	"Early Morning Boogie"	
449	"Evil-Hearted Woman"	1955
456	"My Baby's Gone"	
465	"Blues for My Cookie"	
471	"Hopkins' Sky Hop"	
476	"Grandma's Boogie"	1956
483	"That's All Right Baby"	
490	"Shine On Moon"	
497	"Please Don't Go Baby"	
520	"Bad Boogie"	1957
	(also on Ace 516)	

Joe Turner:
Aladdin
    3013   "Low-Down Dog"   1949
    3077   "Back-Breaking Blues"   1951
Imperial
    5083   "Jumpin' Tonight"   1950
    5093   "Lucille"
Bayou
    015   "The Sun Is Shining"
Colonial
    108   "Midnight Rocking"   1951
RPM
    331   "Kansas City Blues"
    345   "Riding Blues"   1952
Dootone
    306   "Richmond Blues"
Atlantic
    939   "Chains of Love"   1951
    949   "Chill Is On"
    960   "Sweet Sixteen"   1952
    970   "Don't You Cry"
    982   "Still in Love"
    1002   "Honey Hush"   1953
    1016   "TV Mama"
    1026   "Shake, Rattle and Roll"   1954
    1040   "Married Woman"
    1053   "Flip, Flop and Fly"   1955
    1069   "Hide and Seek"
    1080   "Chicken and the Hawk"
    1088   "Corrine, Corrina"   1956
    1100   "Lipstick, Powder and Paint"
    1122   "Midnight Special Train"   1957
    1131   "After Awhile"
    1146   "Love Roller Coaster"
    1155   "Trouble in Mind"

1167	"Wee Baby Blues"	1958
1184	"Blues in the Night"	
2034	"Love Oh Careless Love"	1959

Johnny Otis:

Modern

715	"Thursday Nite Blues"	1949
748	"Good Old Blues"	1950

Savoy

730	"Doggin' Blues"	
732	"Turkey Hop"	
743	"Blues Nocturne"	
759	"Deceivin' Blues"	
764	"Wedding Boogie"	
766	"Rockin' Blues"	
775	"I Don't Care"	1951
777	"Gee Baby"	
788	"All Night Long"	
815	"Harlem Nocturne"	
821	"Sunset to Dawn"	
824	"Get Together Blues"	1952

Peacock

1625	"Young Girl"	1954
1636	"Shake It"	
1648	"Sittin' Here Drinkin' "	1955
1675	"Butterball"	

Dig

119	"Hey Hey Hey Hey"	1956
122	"Midnite Creeper"	
131	"Tough Enough"	
132	"Turtle Dove"	
134	"Wa Wa"	

Capitol

3799	"Hum Ding-A-Ling"	1957
3800	"In the Dark"	
3801	"Tell Me So"	

3852	"Good Golly"	1958
3966	"Willie and the Hand Jive"	
4060	"Crazy Country Hop"	1959
4168	"Castin' My Spell"	

Lowell Fulson:

Swingtime

196	"Every Day I Have the Blues"	1950
226	"Blue Shadows"	
242	"Lonesome Christmas"	
243	"I'm a Nite Owl	1951
295	"Guitar Shuffle"	
320	"Ride Until the Sun Goes Down"	1952
330	"The Blues Come Rollin' In"	
338	"Juke Box Shuffle"	
	(also on Parrot 787)	

Checker

804	"Reconsider Baby"	1955
812	"Check Yourself"	
820	"Lonely Hours"	
829	"Trouble, Trouble"	1956
841	"Tollin' Blues"	
854	"Baby Please Don't Go"	

Smiley Lewis:

Imperial

5072	"Growing Old"	1950
5124	"My Baby Was Right"	1951
5194	"The Bells Are Ringing"	1952
5208	"Gumbo Blues"	
5234	"Play Girl"	1953
5241	"Caldonia's Party"	
5242	"Little Fernandez"	
5268	"Blue Monday"	1954
5279	"I Love You for Sentimental Reasons"	
5296	"That Certain Door"	
5316	"Too Many Drivers"	

5325	"Jailbird"	1955
5356	"I Hear You Knockin' "	
5372	"Come On"	
5380	"One Night"	1956
5389	"She's Got Me"	
5404	"Someday You'll Want Me"	
5418	"No, No"	
5431	"You Are My Sunshine"	1957
5450	"Goin' to Jump and Shout"	
5478	"Bad Luck Blues"	

Little Walter:

Chance

1116	"Ora Nelle Blues"	1950

Checker

758	"Juke"	1952
764	"Mean Old World"	
767	"Don't Have to Hunt No More"	1953
770	"Off the Wall"	
780	"Blues with a Feeling"	1954
786	"You're So Fine"	
793	"Rocker"	
799	"You'd Better Watch Yourself"	
805	"Mellow Down Easy"	1955
811	"My Babe"	
817	"Roller Coaster"	
825	"Too Late"	1956
833	"Who"	
838	"One More Chance with You"	
845	"Just a Feeling"	
852	"Too Late Brother"	1957
859	"Nobody But You"	
867	"Boom Out Goes the Lights"	1958
890	"Confessin' the Blues"	
904	"Key to the Highway"	

Rufus Thomas:
Talent
    807   "I'll Be a Good Boy"   1950
Chess
    1466   "Night Walkin' Blues"   1952
    1492   "No More Doggin' Around"
    1517   "Juanita"
Sun
    181   "Bear Cat"   1953
    188   "Tigerman"

1951–1955

HISTORY AND SOUND

In 1951, a second-generation of country blues singers began recording. The two significant blues vocalists were Howlin' Wolf, a rough, unpolished performer, and the intense Elmore James. Wolf's hit record was "Smokestack Lightning"—his howling voice complemented his low-down guitar style. Elmore James first record was the classic "Dust My Broom"—featuring an uncompromising guitar performance with an electrifying, forceful vocal.

Bobby Bland began his career on Modern Records, but his first hits were on Duke, with the 1957 blues recording "Farther up the Road." Little Junior Parker also started with Modern, but his first hit was "Mystery Train" (an early Elvis Presley cover record) on Sun. Parker's best recording is the rocker "I Wanna Ramble." He recorded several other blues hits throughout the 50's. Arthur Gunter's double-entendre "Baby Let's Play House" (covered by Elvis) was his only hit. Peppermint Harris did well with the downbeat "I Got Loaded," a very popular blues hit. Willie Mae "Big Mama" Thornton started a minor craze with her original "Hound Dog" (an enormous hit for—

you guessed it—Elvis). Johnny Watson recorded some early blues for Federal Records, but his first hit was the RPM release "Those Lonely, Lonely Nights."

Fast cars became a popular subject during this era. Jackie Brenston's "Rocket 88" and Todd Rhodes' "Rocket 69" were both rhythm and blues hits. Rhodes was a band leader who first recorded La Vern Baker.

La Vern Baker and Faye Adams were two important early female vocalists. Faye Adams recorded "Shake a Hand," a powerful, gospel-derived vocal, while La Vern Baker's "Tweedle Dee" became a major rock and roll hit in the mid-50's.

Joe Turner's "Shake, Rattle and Roll," along with "Tweedle Dee," marked the commercial success of rock and roll. Another early hit in the rock and roll style was Young Jesse's "Mary Lou" (a 1959 hit for Ronnie Hawkins).

Instrumentals became very popular when Joe Houston scored with a screaming saxaphone in "All Nite Long," truly an exciting record. "Pachuko Hop" by Chuck Higgins was another exciting instrumental, while Wilbert Harrison's "Florida Special" featured a steady rocking guitar and maracas.

Screamin' Jay Hawkins recorded some wild, pounding records, allegedly during a drunken recording session.

Little Willie John was strictly a ballad singer, who produced a long string of hits. His biggest successes were the original "Fever" and "Talk to Me, Talk to Me."

RARITY AND VALUE

Again, the rarest and most sought after records are the country blues releases. The Howlin' Wolf issues on RPM and the very early Chess recordings, the Modern label releases by Bobby Bland and Junior Parker and the Peppermint Harris releases are worth from $15 to $20, and perhaps more. Later records by these and other blues artists are valued in the $10 and below range, while the hits by Bobby Bland and Junior Parker bring less than $5.

DISCOGRAPHY

Jackie Brenston:
Chess

1458	"Rocket 88"	1951
1469	"My Real Gone Rocket"	
1472	"Juiced"	
1496	"Hi Ho Baby"	
1532	"Starvation"	1952

Peppermint Harris:
Aladdin

3097	"I Got Loaded"	1951
3107	"Have Another Drink and Talk with Me"	
3108	"Let the Back Door Hit You"	
3130	"Right Back On"	1952
3141	"There's a Dead Cat on the Line"	
3154	"Hey Little School Girl"	
3177	"Wasted Love"	1953
3183	"Don't Leave Me All Alone"	
3206	"Three Sheets in the Wind"	

Howlin' Wolf:
RPM

333	"Riding in the Moonlight"	1951
340	"Passing My Blues"	
347	"My Baby Stole Off"	

Chess

1479	"Moanin' at Midnight"	1951
1497	"The Wolf Is at Your Door"	
1510	"Mr. Highway Man"	1952
1515	"Saddle My Pony"	
1528	"My Last Affair"	1953
1557	"All Night Boogie"	
1566	"Rockin' Daddy"	1954
1575	"Evil Is Going On"	

1584	"I'll Be Around"	1955
1593	"Who Will Be Next"	
1607	"Come to Me Baby"	
1618	"Smokestack Lightning"	1956
1632	"I Asked for Water"	
1648	"Going Back Home"	1957
1668	"Nature"	
1679	"Sittin' on Top of the World"	1958
1695	"Moanin' for My Baby"	
1712	"I'm Leaving You"	1959
1726	"Howlin' Blues"	
1735	"Mr. Airplane Man"	

Todd Rhodes:
King

| 4469 | "Gin, Gin, Gin" | 1951 |
| 4528 | "Rocket 69" | 1952 |

Willie Mae "Big Mama" Thornton:
Peacock

1567	"Partnership Blues"	1951
1587	"No Jody for Me"	
1603	"Mischievous Boogie"	1952
1612	"Hound Dog"	
1621	"They Call Me Big Mama"	
1626	"I Ain't No Fool Either"	1953
1632	"I Smell a Rat"	
1642	"Stop Hopping on Me"	1954
1647	"Walking Blues"	
1650	"The Fish"	1955
1654	"Tarzan and the Dignified Monkey"	
1681	"Just Like a Dog"	1957

Bobby Bland:
Modern

| 848 | "Crying All Night Long" | 1952 |
| 868 | "Drifting from Town to Town" | |

Duke

105	"Lovin' Blues"	1953
115	"Army Blues"	
141	"It's My Life Baby"	1955
146	"You or None"	
153	"You've Got Bad Intentions"	1956
160	"I Learned My Lesson"	
167	"I Smell Trouble"	
170	"Farther up the Road"	1957
182	"Bobby's Blues"	
185	"Loan a Helping Hand"	
196	"Last Night"	1958

Elmore James:

Trumpet

146	"Dust My Broom"	1952
	(also on Ace 508; Jewel 764)	

Meteor

5000	"I Believe"	1953
5003	"Sinful Woman"	

Checker

777	"Country Boogie"

Flair

1011	"Hawaiian Boogie"	1954
1014	"Make a Little Love"	
1022	"Strange Kinda Feeling"	
1031	"Make My Dreams Come True"	1954
1039	"1839 Blues"	
1048	"Rock My Baby Right"	
1057	"Standing at the Cross Roads"	1955
	(also on Kent 433)	
1062	"Late Hours at Midnight"	
1069	"Happy Home"	
	(also on Kent 331)	
1074	"Dust My Blues"	
	(also on Kent 331)	
1079	"Blues Before Sunrise"	

Modern

983	"Wild about You"	1956

Chief

7001	"Coming Home" (also on Vee Jay 249)	1957
7004	"It Hurts Me Too" (also on Vee Jay 259)	
7006	"Cry for Me Baby" (also on Vee Jay 269)	

Chess

1756	"The Sun Is Shining"	1959

Fire

1011	"Make My Dreams Come True"	
1016	"The Sky Is Crying"	

Little Junior Parker:

Modern

864	"Bad Women, Bad Whiskey"	1952

Sun

187	"Fussin' and Fightin' "	1953
192	"Mystery Train"	

Duke

120	"Dirty Friend Blues"	1954
127	"Sittin', Drinkin' and Thinkin' "	
137	"I Wanna Ramble"	1955
147	"Driving Me Mad"	
157	"Mother-in-Law Blues"	1956
164	"Next Time You See Me"	
168	"That's Alright"	
177	"Peaches"	1957
184	"Sitting and Thinking"	
193	"Barefoot Rock"	1958
301	"Sweet Home Chicago"	

Faye Adams:

Herald

416	"Shake a Hand"	1953
419	"I'll Be True"	

423	"Say a Prayer"	
429	"Somebody Somewhere"	1954
434	"Hurts Me to My Heart"	

La Vern Baker:

King

4556	"Trying"	1953
4601	"Lost Child"	

Atlantic

1004	"Soul on Fire"	1954
1030	"I Can't Hold Out Any Longer"	
1047	"Tweedle Dee"	
1057	"Bop Ting-A-Ling"	1955
1075	"Play It Fair"	
1087	"Get Up, Get Up"	
1093	"Fee Fee Fi Fo Fum"	1956
1104	"I Can't Love You Enough"	
1116	"Jim Dandy"	
1136	"Jim Dandy Got Married"	1957
1150	"Humpty Dumpty Heart"	
1163	"St. Louis Blues"	
1176	"Substitute"	1958
1189	"Harbor Lights"	
2001	"It's So Fine"	
2007	"I Cried a Tear"	1959
2021	"I Waited Too Long"	
2033	"So High, So Low"	
2041	"Tiny Tim"	

Wilbert Harrison:

Rockin'

526	"This Woman of Mine"	1953
	(also on DeLuxe 6002)	

DeLuxe

6031	"Gin and Coconut Milk"	1954

Savoy

1138	"Don't Drop It"	
1149	"Women and Whiskey"	1955

1164	"Florida Special"	
1198	"Confessin' My Dream"	1956

Fury

1023	"Kansas City"	1959
1031	"C. C. Rider"	
1041	"The Horse"	
1055	"Drafted"	
1059	"Let's Stick Together"	

Johnny Watson:

Federal

12120	"Highway 60"	1953
12175	"Half Pint a Whiskey"	1954
12183	"You Can't Take It with You"	

RPM

423	"Hot Little Mama"	
431	"Too Tired"	1955
436	"Those Lonely, Lonely Nights"	
447	"Oh Baby"	
455	"Three Hours Past Midnight"	1956
471	"Love Me Baby"	

Screamin' Jay Hawkins:

Timely

1004	"Baptize Me in Wine"	1954
	(also on Apollo 528)	
1005	"I Found My Way to Wine"	

Okeh

7072	"I Put a Spell on You"	1956
7087	"Frenzy"	1957
7101	"Alligator Wine"	

Joe Houston:

Money

203	"All Nite Long"	1954

Young Jesse:

Modern

921	"I Smell a Rat"	1954
961	"Mary Lou"	1955

Arthur Gunter:

Excello

2047	"Baby Let's Play House"	1955
2053	"You Are Doing Me Wrong"	
2058	"No Happy Home"	1956
2073	"Baby You Better Listen"	

Chuck Higgins:

Combo

12	"Pachuko Hop"	1955
48	"I'm in Love with You"	
140	"The Duck Walk"	1956

Little Willie John:

King

4818	"All Around the World"	1955
4841	"Need Your Love So Bad"	
4893	"I'm Stickin' with You Baby"	1956
4935	"Fever"	
4960	"Do Something for Me"	
4989	"Suffering with the Blues"	1957
5003	"A Little Bit of Loving"	
5023	"Love Life and Money"	
5045	"I've Got to Cry"	
5066	"Young Girl"	1958
5083	"Dinner Date"	
5091	"Until You Do"	
5108	"Talk to Me, Talk to Me"	
5147	"Tell It Like It Is"	1959

1956–1959

HISTORY AND SOUND

Rock and roll continued, most successfully performed by some New Orleans–influenced performers. A rocking piano beat is apparent in the recordings of Huey "Piano" Smith and Clarence "Frogman" Henry. "Ain't Got No Home" and "Lonely Tramp" by Clarence Henry are very aggressive vocal workouts, heavily influenced by early Fats Domino rockers. Huey Smith was the house pianist for Ace Records. His hit, with vocalist Bobby Marchan, was the very popular "Rockin' Pneumonia and the Boogie Woogie Flu." Smith also played piano on Frankie Ford's unstoppable "Sea Cruise." In 1959, Jesse Hill and Phil Phillips both scored with hits. Hill's "Ooh Poo Pah Doo" is a screaming vocal with an excellent rock and roll accompaniment. "Sea of Love" by Phil Phillips is a medium-tempo recording with a hypnotic background accompaniment.

Rock and roll instrumentals continued to be popular. Bill Doggett's "Honky Tonk" was one of the best-sellers of 1956, while Ernie Freeman's piano rocker "Raunchy" was a major 1957 smash. Both records were the best-selling rhythm and blues instrumentals of the decade. In 1956, Billy Stewart recorded the fine "Billy's Blues."

In 1957, Specialty Records introduced Larry Williams, who recorded some fine rock and roll records. Williams' style was drawn somewhat from the exciting vocal performances of Little Richard.

Though the late 50's is usually considered the era of the rock and roll singer, some fine blues were also recorded. Slim Harpo did "I'm a King Bee," a fine blues number in a droning guitar style. His best-seller was the 1961 top-ten hit "Rainin' in My Heart." In 1959, Buster Brown recorded the great harmonica rocker "Fannie Mae." Big Jay McNeeley's hit was the down-tempo piano blues "There Is Something on Your Mind."

RARITY AND VALUE

The rarest of these single-artist discs are the earliest recording by Huey Smith, "Little Liza Jane," and "I'm a King Bee" by Slim Harpo, both worth a bit in excess of $5. None of the other recordings from this era bring more than $5, with some smash hits, including Ernie Freeman's "Raunchy" and Bill Doggett's "Honky Tonk," worth only $1 or $2.

DISCOGRAPHY

Bill Doggett:
King

4950	"Honky Tonk"	1956

Clarence Henry:
Argo

5259	"Ain't Got No Home"	1956
5266	"Lonely Tramp"	
5273	"I Found a Home"	

Huey Smith:
Ace

521	"Little Liza Jane"	1956
530	"Rockin' Pneumonia and the Boogie Woogie Flu"	1957
538	"Just a Lonely Clown"	
545	"Don't You Just Know It"	1958
548	"Having a Good Time"	
553	"Don't You Know Yockomo"	
562	"Genevieve"	1959
571	"Tu-ber-cu-luca and the Sinus Blues"	
584	"Beatnick Blues"	

Billy Stewart:
Chess

1625	"Billy's Blues"	1956

Okeh

7095	"Billy's Heartache"	1957

Ernie Freeman:
Cash

1017	"Jivin' Around"	1957

Imperial
    5474   "Raunchy"
  Slim Harpo:
Excello

2113	"I'm a King Bee"	1957
2138	"Wonderin' and Worryin' "	1958
2162	"You'll Be Sorry One Day"	1959
2171	"Buzz Me Babe"	

  Larry Williams:
Specialty

597	"Just Because"	1957
608	"Short Fat Fannie"	
615	"Bony Maronie"	
626	"Dizzy Miss Lizzie"	1958
634	"Hootchy Koo"	
647	"Peaches and Cream"	
658	"She Said 'Yeah' "	1959
665	"Steal a Little Kiss"	
677	"Give Me Love"	
682	"Little School Girl"	

  Buster Brown:
Fire

1008	"Fannie Mae"	1959
1020	"John Henry"	
1023	"Is You Is or Is You Ain't My Baby"	

  Jessie Hill:
Minit

607	"Ooh Poo Pah Doo"	1959

  Big Jay McNeeley:
Swingin'

614	"There Is Something on Your Mind"	1959

  Phil Phillips:

71459	"Sea of Love"	1959

ROCK AND ROLL-ROCKABILLY

White rock and roll—rockabilly—was a relatively late musical innovation in the 50's. This merging of country and western with rhythm and blues music took hold as record companies and radio stations became aware of the increasing interest on the part of young record buyers—both black and white—in the previously suppressed Negro rhythm and blues. It was an attempt on the part of record companies to cash in on the coming trend. It was also an effort by the media to suppress "dirty and inferior" rhythm and blues by siphoning off the audience. It did not work. With the increased popularity of rock and roll, rhythm and blues music became more appreciated and successful in its own right.

The earliest rock and roll performer was Bill Haley. After Haley's rock and roll sound became established, Sun Records of Memphis pioneered the rockabilly sound of Elvis Presley, Carl Perkins and Jerry Lee Lewis. In fact, rockabilly is often called the "Sun sound," even though not all of this music was issued on the Sun label. Elvis Presley was the earliest exponent of Sun rockabilly, drawing heavily from blues artists Arthur Crudup, Lonnie Johnson and Arthur Gunter. These spontaneous Sun recordings are a far cry from the smoother RCA waxings.

It is from these origins that much of later white rock and roll is drawn.

Bill Haley and the Comets

HISTORY AND SOUND

Bill Haley was originally a country and western entertainer and overtones of this style are apparent in his recordings. He was the first white singer to successfully record rock and roll in his early issues, including "Rocket 88" (a Jackie Brenston original) and "Crazy, Man, Crazy." Haley's "Rock Around the Clock" was the first honest-to-god rock and roll song to achieve hit status. It was a singularly influential record in that it boldly introduced rock and roll to a previously unaware record-buying public. "Rock Around the Clock" proved a rude awakening to most popular-music-loving Americans—their music was never again to be the same. From this strong impetus, Haley managed to record good-sellers for the next two years. However, he could not sustain his popularity, which diminished with the rising fortunes of such attractive and dynamic rock and roll performers as Elvis Presley and Little Richard. Bill Haley faded, but rock and roll advanced.

RARITY AND VALUE

The Holiday and early Essex label releases, particularly "Rock the Joint" and "Rocket 88," are rare, worth over $15. None of the Decca issues are rare, bringing only $1 or $2 at most.

DISCOGRAPHY

Holiday
    105   "Rocket 88"/"Tearstains on My Heart"   1952
Essex
    303   "Rock the Joint"/"Farewell, So Long, Goodbye"
    310   "Real Rock Drive"

321   "Crazy, Man, Crazy"/"Whatcha Gonna Do" 1953
327   "Fractured"/"Pat a Cake"
332   "Live It Up"/"Farewell, So Long, Goodbye" 1954
340   "Ten Little Indians"/"I'll Be True"
348   "Chatanooga Choo Choo"
374   "Sundown Boogie"/"Juke Box Cannonball"   1955
381   "Rocket 88"
399   "Rock the Joint"

Trans World
718   "Real Rock Drive"/"Yes Indeed"

Decca
29124   "Rock Around the Clock"/"Thirteen Women" 1955
29209   "Shake, Rattle and Roll"/"ABC Boogie"
29317   "Dim, Dim the Lights"/"Happy Baby"
29418   "Birth of the Boogie"/"Mambo Rock"
29552   "Two Hound Dogs"/"Razzle Dazzle"
29713   "Rock-A-Beatin' Boogie"/"Burn That Candle" 1956
29791   "See You Later Alligator"/"Paper Boy"
29870   "R-O-C-K"/"Saints' Rock and Roll"
29948   "Rockin' Through the Rye"/"Hot Dog
         Buddy Buddy"
30028   "Rip It Up"/"Teenager's Mother"
30085   "Rudy's Rock"/"Blue Comet Blues"   1957
30148   "Don't Knock the Rock"/
         "Choo Choo Ch'Boogie"
30214   "Hook, Line and Sinker"/"Forty Cups of Coffee"
30314   "Rockin' Rollin' Rover"/"Billy Goat"
30394   "The Dipsy Doodle"/"How Many"

Elvis Presley

HISTORY AND SOUND

Sun Records originally specialized in the blues. Shortly after its founding in 1953, the Sun artist roster included Rufus

Thomas, Little Junior Parker, James Cotton and Little Milton. However it was with the issue of Sun record #209, "That's All Right" (written by blues artist Arthur "Big Boy" Crudup), backed with the country classic "Blue Moon of Kentucky," that Sun Records took off. This record was recorded by young Elvis Aaron Presley. Elvis made five Sun records, each an excellent example of early rockabilly, before his contract was purchased by RCA Records. From that point his career is legend. The Sun issues and several of the early RCA releases, including "Blue Suede Shoes" and "One-Sided Love Affair," are fine rockabilly recordings. However, as Elvis' popularity skyrocketed, his style became more polished, and his performances lost their blues and rockabilly edge. From "Love Me Tender" on, his releases were either pop ballads or sophisticated rock and roll.

RARITY AND VALUE

All of the Elvis Presley Sun releases are in great demand by record collectors throughout the world. In fact, the value of these discs exceeds the value of almost any other record by any other 50's single artist. The price for a Sun 45 RPM issue varies from $50 to $100—the least rare is "Mystery Train," the rarest are the first two Sun records. The earliest RCA releases, the Sun reissues and the series from RCA 6636–43, bring around $2. No later Elvis Presley release is difficult to find, and thus value is even more limited.

DISCOGRAPHY

Sun

209	"That's All Right"/"Blue Moon of Kentucky" (also on RCA 6380)	1954
210	"Good Rockin' Tonight"/"I Don't Care if the Sun Don't Shine" (also on RCA 6381)	
215	"Milkcow Blues Boogie"/"You're a Heartbreaker" (also on RCA 6382)	1955

| 217 | "Baby Let's Play House"/"I'm Left, You're Right, She's Gone" (also on RCA 6383) | |
| 223 | "Mystery Train"/"I Forgot to Remember to Forget" (also on RCA 6357) | |

RCA

6420	"Heartbreak Hotel"/"I Was the One"	1956
6540	"I Want You, I Need You, I Love You"/"My Baby Left Me"	
6604	"Hound Dog"/"Don't Be Cruel"	
6636	"Blue Suede Shoes"/"Tutti Frutti"	
6637	"I Got a Woman"/"I'm Countin' on You"	
6638	"I'm Gonna Sit Right Down and Cry"/"I'll Never Let You Go"	
6639	"Tryin' to Get to You"/"I Love You Because"	
6640	"Just Because"/"Blue Moon"	
6641	"Money Honey"/"One-Sided Love Affair"	
6642	"Shake, Rattle and Roll"/"Lawdy Miss Clawdy"	
6643	"Love Me Tender"/"Anyway You Want Me"	
6800	"Too Much"/"Playing for Keeps"	1957
6870	"All Shook Up"/"That's When Your Heartaches Begin"	
7000	"Teddy Bear"/"Loving You"	
7035	"Jailhouse Rock"/"Treat Me Nice"	
7150	"I Beg of You"/"Don't"	
7240	"Wear My Ring around Your Neck"/"Doncha Think It's Time"	1958
7280	"Hard-Headed Woman"/"Don't Ask Me Why"	
7410	"One Night"/"I Got Stung"	
7506	"A Fool Such as I"/"I Need Your Love Tonight"	1959
7600	"A Big Hunk o' Love"/"My Wish Came True"	

Carl Perkins

HISTORY AND SOUND

Carl Perkins was the second Sun label rockabilly artist, recorded in a hope of recreating the success of Elvis Presley, after Elvis had departed for RCA. In fact, Carl Perkins did have several successful records, but his career did not reach superstar proportions. His style remained classic rockabilly, especially in the fine "Blue Suede Shoes" (later recorded by Elvis) and "Matchbox" (a 60's hit for the Beatles). Perkins' career was interrupted by an auto accident in 1957. He returned as a country and western singer for Columbia Records in the early 60's.

RARITY AND VALUE

The rarest Perkins records are "Movie Magg," "Let the Jukebox Keep on Playing" and "Sure to Fall" (the last reportedly was either not issued or withdrawn at issue). The three are valued in the $50 area. The remainder of Carl Perkins' releases bring under $5.

DISCOGRAPHY

Flip

501	"Movie Magg"/"Turn Around"	1954

Sun

224	"Let the Jukebox Keep on Playing"/	
	"Gone, Gone, Gone"	1955
234	"Blue Suede Shoes"/"Honey Don't"	
235	"Sure to Fall"/"Tennessee"	
243	"Boppin' the Blues"/"All Mama's Children"	

249	"Dixie Fried"/"I'm Sorry I'm Not Sorry"	1956
261	"Matchbox"/"Your True Love"	
274	"Forever Yours"/"That's Right"	1957

Jerry Lee Lewis and his Pumping Piano

HISTORY AND SOUND

The third important Sun rockabilly artist, Jerry Lee Lewis' first record was the country and western ballad "Crazy Arms." However, Lewis became a rock and roll sensation with his exciting piano and vocal workouts in "Whole Lotta Shakin' Goin' On," "Great Balls of Fire" and "Breathless." He returned to recording country and western songs in the 60's, managing to reestablish his star status. However, "Whole Lotta Shakin' Goin' On" and "Great Balls of Fire" remain as two of the best and most original rock and roll releases of the 50's.

RARITY AND VALUE

None of the Jerry Lee Lewis recordings are rare or bring high prices, as most were good-selling hits. "Crazy Arms" can bring up to $5, latter issues are worth $2 or $3.

DISCOGRAPHY

Sun

259	"Crazy Arms"/"End of the Road"	1956
267	"Whole Lotta Shakin' Goin' On"/	
	"It'll Be Me"	1957
281	"Great Balls of Fire"/"You Win Again"	
288	"Breathless"/"Down the Line"	1958

296   "High School Confidential"/"Fools Like Me"
301   "Lewis Boogie"/"The Return of Jerry Lee"
303   "Break Up"/"I'll Make It All up to You"   1959
312   "I'll Sail My Ship Alone"/"It Hurts Me So"
317   "Lovin' up a Storm"/"Big Blon' Baby"
324   "Let's Talk About Us"/"Ballad of Billy Joe"
330   "Little Queenie"/"I Could Never Be
        Ashamed of You"

Buddy Holly / The Crickets

HISTORY AND SOUND

Buddy Holly's recording career began with some poor-selling Decca releases in 1956. Although these sides were recorded in his distinctive rocking guitar and vocal style, Holly's sound didn't become popular until 1957. Recording for Coral as Buddy Holly and for Brunswick as the Crickets, Buddy Holly and his back-up band, the Crickets, scored with several major hits. "That'll Be the Day" and the next two releases by the "chirpin' " Crickets were top-ten rock and roll hits. "Peggy Sue," a Buddy Holly release that featured a throbbing guitar beat and emotional Holly vocal performance, was his biggest hit and sold well for years. The flip side of "Peggy Sue," "Everyday," was a strongly felt uptempo ballad. In fact, "That'll Be the Day" and "Peggy Sue" were two of the very best rock and roll records of the decade. Buddy Holly attracted legions of fans throughout his recording career, becoming something of a legendary figure after his death in 1959 in an accident that also claimed Ritchie Valens and J. P. Richardson—the Big Bopper. The legend has not diminished. To this day, Buddy Holly fans consider him the most important rock and roll artist of the 50's.

RARITY AND VALUE

The rarest Buddy Holly records are the Decca releases. They generally bring prices in excess of $10 to $15 from an avowed Holly collector. The Coral and Brunswick issues all sold well and are generally worth less than $5.

DISCOGRAPHY

Decca

29854	"Blue Days, Black Nights"/"Love Me"	1956
30166	"Modern Don Juan"/"You Are My One Desire"	
30434	"That'll Be the Day"/"Rock Around Ollie Vee"	1957
30543	"You Are My One Desire"/"Love Me"	
30650	"Ting-A-Ling"/"Girl on My Mind"	

Coral

61852	"Words of Love"/"Mailman Bring Me No More Blues"	1957
61885	"Peggy Sue"/"Everyday"	
61942	"Rave On"/"Take Your Time"	1958
62006	"Early in the Morning"/"Now We're One"	
62052	"Heartbeat"/"Well . . . All Right"	
62074	"Raining in My Heart"/"It Doesn't Matter Anymore"	1959
62134	"Peggy Sue Got Married"/"Crying, Waiting, Hoping"	
62210	"True Love Ways"/"That Makes It Tough"	
62329	"Reminiscing"/"Wait Till the Sun Shines Nellie"	
62352	"True Love Ways"/"Bo Diddley"	
62369	"Brown-Eyed Handsome Man"/"Wishing"	
62390	"Rock Around Ollie Vee"/"I'm Gonna Love You Too"	

62448	"Slippin' and Slidin' "/"What to Do"	
62558	"Love Is Strange"/"You Are the One"	

As by the Crickets:

Brunswick

55009	"That'll Be the Day"/"I'm Lookin' for Someone to Love"	1957
55035	"Oh Boy"/"Not Fade Away"	
55053	"Maybe Baby"/"Tell Me Now"	1958
55072	"Think It Over"/"Fool's Paradise"	
55094	"It's So Easy"/"Lonesome Tears"	
55124	"Love's Made a Fool of You"/"Someone, Someone"	1959
55153	"When You Ask about Love"/"Deborah"	

Coral

62198	"More Than I Can Say"/"Baby My Heart"

Gene Vincent and his Blue Caps

HISTORY AND SOUND

Gene Vincent recorded consistent rock and roll, from his classic "Be-Bop-A-Lula" to the equally strong "Lotta Lovin'." He and his group, the Blue Caps, produced a fine rock and roll sound on record and on stage. Handicapped and quite underweight, Gene Vincent's stage presence was that of a stark, tragic figure. This unusual quality attracted a number of admiring fans, second only to the horde of Buddy Holly followers, whose admiration persists even after Vincent's death in 1971.

RARITY AND VALUE

All of Gene Vincent's releases sold well and now bring less than $5.

DISCOGRAPHY

Capitol

3450	"Be-Bop-A-Lula"/"Woman Love"	1956
3530	"Race with the Devil"/"Gonna Back up Baby"	
3558	"Blue Jean Bop"/"Who Slapped John"	
3617	"Crazy Legs"/"Important Words"	1957
3678	"Five Days, Five Days"/"Bi Bichey Bo Bo"	
3763	"Lotta Lovin' "/"Wear My Ring"	
3839	"Dance to the Bop"/"I Got It"	
3959	"Baby Blue"/"True to You"	1958
4010	"Rocky Road Blues"/"Yes I Love You Baby"	
4105	"Be Bop Boogie Boy"/"Say Mama"	1959

Eddie Cochran

HISTORY AND SOUND

Eddie Cochran's early rockabilly ballad style is evident in his first Liberty Records release, "Sittin' in the Balcony." Cochran also recorded some fine rock and roll, including "Mean When I'm Mad," but his first major hit was the 1958 classic rocker "Summertime Blues." Two follow-up releases were also good-selling rock and roll records, the steamrollers "C'mon Everybody" and "Somethin' Else." As with so many of his contemporaries, Cochran was killed in a 1959 auto accident, while on tour in Europe.

RARITY AND VALUE

The Crest release and the earliest Liberty releases are worth between $5 and $10. "Summertime Blues" and later Liberty issues bring from $2 to $5.

DISCOGRAPHY

Crest
1026	"Skinny Jim"/"Half Loved"	1956

Liberty
55056	"Sittin' in the Balcony"/"Dark Lonely Street"	1957
55070	"Mean When I'm Mad"/"One Kiss"	
55087	"Drive-in Show"/"Am I Blue"	
55112	"Twenty-Flight Rock"/"Cradle Baby"	
55123	"Jeannie, Jeannie, Jeannie"/"Pocketful of Heartaches"	1958
55138	"Pretty Girl"/"Theresa"	
55144	"Summertime Blues"/"Love Again"	
55166	"C'mon Everybody"/"Don't Ever Let Me Go"	
55177	"Teenage Heaven"/"I Remember"	1959
55203	"Somethin' Else"/"Boll Weevil Song"	
55217	"Little Angel"/"Hallelujah I Love Her So"	
55242	"Cut Across Shorty"/"Five Steps to Heaven"	

The Everly Brothers

HISTORY AND SOUND

Don and Phil Everly first recorded the appealing country-influenced rockers "Bye Bye Love" and "Wake up Little Susie," both major 1957 hits. Their first ballad, "All I Have to Do Is Dream," was one of the best-selling records of 1958, as was the follow-up, the effective rocker "Bird Dog." The Everly Brothers' string of hits continued well into the 60's.

RARITY AND VALUE

None of the records by the Everly Brothers are rare, and thus bring $2 at most.

DISCOGRAPHY

Cadence

1315	"Bye Bye Love"/"I Wonder if I Care Too Much"	1957
1337	"Wake up Little Susie"/"Maybe Tomorrow"	
1342	"This Little Girl of Mine"/"Should We Tell Him"	
1348	"All I Have to Do Is Dream"/"Claudette"	1958
1350	"Bird Dog"/"Devoted to You"	
1355	"Problems"/"Love of My Life"	
1364	"Poor Jenny"/"Take a Message to Mary"	1959
1369	"Till I Kissed You"/"Oh What a Feeling"	
1376	"Let It Be Me"/"Since You Broke My Heart"	
1380	"Be Bop A Lula"/"When Will I Be Loved"	

Ritchie Valens

HISTORY AND SOUND

Ritchie Valens first recorded for the small Los Angeles Del Fi label in 1958. His initial release was the mild-selling "Come On, Let's Go," a driving, shouting rocker. Valens' first ballad release, "Donna," with the rocking flip, "La Bamba," catapulted the young singer to instant stardom. "Donna" is a fine, emotionally rendered love song, one of the memorable rock and roll performances of the 50's. "That's My Little Susie" was Valens' last release before his 1959 death in a plane crash. Valens attracted a great number of fans during his very short career and became even more popular after his death. "We Belong Together" and later releases were issued on a Del Fi "Memorial Series" label. All sold well.

RARITY AND VALUE

In the years immediately after Ritchie Valens' death, the prices of the 45's and LP's were unrealistically inflated—one LP reportedly sold for over $100. The continuing popularity of his records means that none are now rare, and most of the 45 RPM releases can now be obtained for less than $5.

DISCOGRAPHY

Del Fi

4106	"Come On, Let's Go"/"Framed"	1958
4110	"Donna"/"La Bamba"	
4111	"Fast Freight"/"Big Baby Blues"	
4114	"That's My Little Susie"/"In a Turkish Town"	1959
4117	"We Belong Together"/"Little Girl"	
4128	"Stay Beside Me"/"Big Baby Blues"	
4133	"Cry, Cry, Cry"/"Paddiwack Song"	

NOTABLE ROCK AND
ROLL-ROCKABILLY ARTISTS

1955–1959

HISTORY AND SOUND

Roy Orbison, a fine Sun Records artist, recorded some remarkable rockabilly. His "Ooby Dooby" is an early classic, later to be recorded by Creedence Clearwater. In the 60's, Orbison achieved commercial success with such melancholy rockers as "Only the Lonely" and "Leah" on Monument Records.

The Johnny Burnette Trio recorded some fine, flat-out rock and roll. Several of their better recordings are "Drinkin' Wine Spo-Dee-O-Dee" (a Sticks McGhee original) and "Honey Hush" (originally by Joe Turner), both very fine rockabilly renditions of these rhythm and blues classics.

Not until 1957 did rockabilly performers begin to record original compositions instead of relying on previous rhythm and blues successes. There were early notable exceptions to this imitative process, namely, Gene Vincent's "Be Bop A Lula" and Carl Perkins' "Blue Suede Shoes," and later compositions by these performers. Too often, however, early rock and roll releases, including Bill Haley's "Rocket 88" and several of the Johnny Burnette Trio releases, though fine recordings, were derivative. However, by late 1957, the popularity of the cover record diminished considerably as rhythm and blues artists began to receive full credit for their performances. At this point, white rock and roll artists began recording their own material.

Three very successful rock and roll singers began their careers in 1957. Conway Twitty recorded two records for Mercury, but did not score until 1958 with his MGM release "It's Only Make Believe," an effective weeping ballad. Twitty became a major country and western talent in the late 60's. Jack Scott first recorded for ABC Records. His tough, growling style became popular with the 1958 recording "My True Love," his first solid hit. His most compelling records are the strong "Goodbye Baby" and the menacing "The Way I Walk," both featuring powerful guitar work. Dale Hawkins scored with his first rocking release, "Suzy Q" (also the first hit for Creedence Clearwater ten years later), and continued to record such driving rockers as "La Doo Da Da" and "Class Cutter."

In 1958, the Big Bopper recorded his best-selling "Chantilly Lace," a rock and roll vaudeville performance. The rock and roll instrumental was at its greatest popularity with the fine guitar work of "Tequila" by the Champs, the full sounds of Duane Eddy's band in "Movin' 'n' Groovin'," and the tough, tight Link Wray record "Rumble," a guitar classic.

In 1959, Ronnie Hawkins and the Hawks (the Hawks later backed Bob Dylan as the Band) reprised Young Jessie's "Mary Lou" in a fine rock and roll performance. Frankie Ford used Huey "Piano" Smith's fine band to best advantage in his non-stop rocker "Sea Cruise."

RARITY AND VALUE

The rarest of these rock and roll releases are the Roy Orbison Jewel and the Johnny Burnette Trio Coral releases, both worth over $10. Records by Roy Orbison on Sun, the Big Bopper on D, Conway Twitty on Mercury, Jack Scott on ABC and early Dale Hawkins on Checker all bring from $5 to $10, occasionally in excess of $10. Other early rock and roll releases generally are worth under $5, especially the later hits by the Big Bopper on Mercury and Frankie Ford on Ace.

DISCOGRAPHY

Roy Orbison:
Jewel
    101   "Ooby Dooby"   1955
Sun
    242   "Ooby Dooby"
    251   "You're My Baby"   1956
    265   "Sweet and Easy"   1957
            (also on Sun 353)
    284   "Chicken-Hearted"
RCA
    7381   "Sweet and Innocent"   1958
Johnny Burnette Trio:
Coral
    61651   "Tear It Up"   1956
    61719   "Honey Hush"
    61758   "Lonesome Train"
    61829   "Eager Beaver"   1957
    61869   "Drinkin' Wine Spo Dee O Dee"
    61918   "Rockabilly Boogie"   1958
Conway Twitty:
Mercury
    71086   "I Need Your Lovin'"   1957
    71384   "Double Talk Baby"   1958
MGM
    12677   "It's Only Make Believe"
    12748   "The Story of My Love"
    12784   "Hey Little Lucy"
    12804   "Mona Lisa"   1959
    12820   "Danny Boy"
    12857   "Lonely Blue Boy"
Jack Scott:
ABC
    9818   "Baby She' Gone"   1957

Carlton
 462 "My True Love" 1958
 483 "With Your Love"
 493 "Goodbye Baby"
 504 "Bella" 1959
 514 "The Way I Walk"
 519 "There Comes a Time"
 Dale Hawkins:
Checker
 843 "See You Soon Baboon" 1957
 863 "Suzy Q"
 876 "Baby, Baby" 1958
 892 "Tornado"
 900 "La Doo Da Da"
 906 "A House, a Car and a Wedding Ring" 1959
 913 "Someday, One Day"
 916 "Class Cutter"
 923 "Ain't That Lovin' You Baby"
 929 "Lifeguard Man"
 934 "Liza Jane"
 Big Bopper:
D
 1008 "Chantilly Lace" 1958
  (also on Mercury 71343)
Mercury
 71375 "Little Red Riding Hood"
 71416 "Somebody Watching over You"
 The Champs:
Challenge
 1016 "Tequila" 1958
 Duane Eddy and the Rebels:
Jamie
 1101 "Movin' 'n' Groovin' " 1958
 Link Wray and the Wray Men:
Cadence
 1347 "Rumble" 1958

Frankie Ford
Ace

549	"Cheatin' Woman"	1958
554	"Sea Cruise"	1959
566	"Alimony"	

Ronnie Hawkins and His Hawks:
Roulette

4154	"Forty Days"	1959
4177	"Mary Lou"	

SOURCES

Many established collectors believe that the earlier, rare releases by the better rhythm and blues/rock and roll artists are about impossible to obtain, especially on a 45 RPM disc, and that when available, the costs are astronomical. As a consequence, they will advise the beginning collector to pay these high prices, or settle for a tape, an LP cut or a bootleg. Nonsense!

Such original recordings are expensive, if one limits himself—as many of these collectors do—to the auction or record-dealer-list form of buying. However, too often the cheapest and often the best sources for originals are ignored—the neighborhood (or out-of-town) junk shop, thrift store, rummage room, garage sale, five-and-dime variety store, swap-meet or long-forgotten warehouses and back rooms of record and jukebox dealers and distributors or the record companies themselves.

Most collectors began collecting by locating records from these sources and have cleaned out many of the choice stocks, but many remain, overlooked and untouched, still full of very rare records. Collectors often become overly sophisticated, preferring to trade or buy from other collectors or dealers, thus inflating prices. In the process, the art of junking and scrounging for records has become almost forgotten.

A Basic Source—The Junk Shop

Junk-shopping is no innovation as far as the hard-core record collector is concerned. He's been buying on a second-hand level for years. There is a systematic approach to junk store record collecting. Put simply, it is: Visit as many junk stores as you can, wherever you can find them, and visit them often.

The successful collector will seek out and identify as many thrift outlets as possible and explore each of these sources for useful records. Generally, these shops feature reasonable prices, from a nickle to a dime per record, good turnover and some unusual records. Although the beginning collector may be disappointed by the number of useful finds, if he persists, rarely will much time go by before a gem turns up.

One major drawback to the junk-shopping approach is that the learning collector tends to purchase a large quantity of actual junk. But this is part of learning what to buy and what to avoid. Overconservative buying of records by only known artists or purchasing just hit records results in bypassing the best finds, the most obscure records. The art of selecting the right records from a thrift store shelf can be developed only by making mistakes. In time the collector develops the ability to tell from the label a desirable rhythm and blues or rock and roll release. There is no rule of thumb because of the great number of obscure artists, labels and releases. However, it does pay to take chances, to buy an unknown record for a few cents. The inevitable stack of mistake purchases you accumulate will hold treasures for another collector with different tastes.

Weekend or extended record-hunting trips can be productive. Whenever visiting out-of-the-way areas, make time to junk-shop. Seeing Miami or Denver by way of the local Goodwill or Salvation Army thrift store may not be the chamber of commerce scenic route, but to the record collector it's mandatory. Find a phone book and a city map, pinpoint the area in which most thrift stores are located, then start looking. You may be lucky.

While purchasing thrift store records, pay close attention to the condition of the wax and label. All too often junk store records are scratched, slightly or badly warped, have scrawled names or initials or nonremovable stickers applied to the label, or may be otherwise mutilated. Even so, a surprising percentage of thrift store records are in reasonably good playing condition and can be enjoyed with only a minimum of disturbing interference caused by the used condition of the record.

One record in only fair, i.e., scratched, condition may be worth purchasing, while another may not. As an example, any 45 RPM record by the Five Keys on the Aladdin label is well worth obtaining, regardless of condition. On the other hand, Little Richard releases on the Specialty label should be purchased in only very good to mint condition because they were extremely popular, and thus are quite commonly available. If you pass up several copies of "Long Tall Sally" in fair or poor condition, you will eventually locate the disc in much better shape. However, if you pass up a copy of "Glory of Love" by the Five Keys, chances are you'll never see it again.

Most records you find in a thrift store are very dirty. An alcohol clean (use a nineteen-cent bottle of rubbing alcohol, apply with a cotton ball) will remove most of the surface grime. The remainder can be wiped off with a soft, nonabrasive cloth. Velvet or a baby's diaper are ideal. Once the dirt is removed, the record should be kept clean by wiping the surface with a nonmagnetic cloth prior to each play. This will prolong the life of the record.

Warps can be removed, but with great caution. Extreme warps can be reduced by heating the affected area, without actually touching the heat source, and then slowly straightening the malleable wax. Don't overheat, and don't press too hard on the wax. The warped area will contract, but the result will often be a better sound and a playable disc.

The Jukebox Dealer, The Record Dealer

Some collectors find well-organized and carefully planned record-hunting trips quite successful. Because of the concentration of collectors in the metropolitan areas, especially in the New York City–Brooklyn and Philadelphia vicinity, it is generally easier for residents of these localities to make major finds by traveling some distance from their homes. Record-hunting trips are most successful with preparation. This involves writing to record and jukebox dealers in outlying areas, describing wants and prearranging visits. By doing this the collector can eliminate the hit-and-miss aspect of a record hunt, though often at the sacrifice of adventure and sponteneity.

Many jukebox dealers and record wholesalers do not encourage visits by the general public. Many of them have been taken advantage of by collectors or are simply too busy to give interested individuals access to the stock. If you do gain admittance, it will usually be because you've convinced the owner that you are prepared to make large purchases. Generally, the larger the purchase, the better the per record price.

Some record merchants are becoming aware of the value recently attached to rarer records. Often, when a collector encounters a valuable find, the dealer will watch him closely as he selects the rarer records and permit him to take only one copy of each—keeping the remaining copies for himself. Thus the dealer learns from the collector which records to hold out and sell at premium prices.

In short, record dealers are getting hip to rare records. Where they once offered ten-cent or three-for-a-quarter displays of unsleeved 45's, they now put the same records in heavy green sleeves, label them as rare and charge $5 and up—often for junk. Be careful. Fortunately such practices are rare.

Other Collectors, Dealerships Owned by Collectors

Lately, dealerships selling only rare records and catering to collectors have been appearing at a rapid rate. Generally, they are located in the New York City–Philadelphia area, where obtaining records from other sources is nearly impossible. But dealers are proliferating and can be found in other Atlantic Coast and West Coast areas.

Most are honest, but several, particularly the mail-order outfits, do employ questionable methods, such as pasting Sun labels on Elvis Presley RCA releases and selling bootlegs or reissues as originals at the original prices. These dealers can occasionally be good sources for fine records, but the often high prices make quantity purchases a very expensive proposition.

When you begin collecting via the junk store or jukebox dealer route, you'll probably meet other collectors seeking the same records you are. Often, one or two local collectors have certain sources staked out and they keep a close and wary eye on these stores. They are suspicious and disapproving of any other collector who may intrude on their turf. Their cardinal rule is: Never tell another collector of a good source.

Sometimes this type of local collector may be able to convince a thrift store or jukebox proprietor for one reason or another that he should have the first pick of any new stock, thus weeding out all the prime records. Other ploys involve giving a soft-hearted Salvation Army cashier a pitch like, "I need some records for some mentally retarded crippled orphans." Collectors often take home a stack of free records with this routine.

Such tactics are not recommended as they make and keep record collecting small time and selfish. Record collecting will grow only as the number of collectors grows.

Instead, meet other collectors. If you encounter another collector shuffling through a stack that you've both found in a thrift store, don't give him a cold stare or an elbow in the ribs. Bring up the subject of your common interest—collecting. He may be your competitor, but then again, your tastes may be widely different. If you, a rhythm and blues collector, meet a rockabilly collector in this situation, he will be glad to take some of your mistake purchases and give up in turn rhythm and blues records he doesn't want. If he's your competitor, you can probably work out mutually advantageous trades. Getting to know other collectors in your area helps keep the art of collecting alive.

Every beginning collector will encounter a more experienced collector who will help himself to some valuable records, and in exchange trade comparatively worthless records. Eventually, the beginner finds he's been taken. One of two major changes occur at this point. He becomes disillusioned and quits collecting; or he gets hip quick and begins cheating less knowledgable collectors. Either way, these reactions keep record collecting a cheap competitive sport. Only better organization among collectors, a clear code of behavior and a universal knowledge of values will solve this problem.

Too often collectors lose sight of what collecting is all about —the sound. A work of art. Well worth seeking and enjoying, not for material value, but for the love of the work of art.

PUBLICATIONS

Recently, a number of magazines designed for the record collector have appeared. Several of the better publications are:

Big Town Review. P.O. Box 406, Flushing, N.Y. 11367. Concentrates on rhythm and blues vocal groups. An extensive records "for sale" list.

Bim Bam Boom, "The Magazine Devoted to the History of Rhythm and Blues." Box 301, Bronx, N.Y. 10469. Concerned almost exclusively with rhythm and blues vocal groups. Provides an extensive record auction and sale list.

Blues Unlimited. 38a Sackville Rd., Bexhill-on-Sea, Sussex, England. The definitive blues publication.

R and B Magazine. C/o Pea-Vine Music, 18632 Nordhoff St., Northridge, California 91324. Covers all aspects of rhythm and blues—from blues and gospel to vocal groups. Record auctions are contained in a separate *Record Market* publication, at the same address.

Record Exchanger, "The Foremost Publication Covering the History of Rock and Roll." Box 2144, Anaheim, California 92804. Specializes in rhythm and blues vocal groups with a secondary emphasis on rock and roll. Publishes an extensive auction list of records.

Shout. 46 Slades Drive, Chislehurst, Kent BR 7 6JX, England. Concentrates on recent soul music, but publishes enough early rhythm and blues material to keep it interesting.

Also, there are assorted discographical publications from which portions of the preceding discographies were drawn:

Blues Records 1943–1966, by Mike Leadbitter and Neil

Slavens, Hanover Books, Ltd., 4 Mill St., London, W.1., 1968. (U.S. agents are Oak Publications, 33 W. 60th St., N.Y. 10023) $15.

Blues Research (pamphlets), published by Record Research, 65 Grand Ave., Brooklyn, N.Y. 11205. Contains discographies on many major blues and rhythm and blues labels.

The Sun Legend, by Paul Vernon. Discographies and descriptions of Sun artists. Can be ordered from *Blues Unlimited*, 38a Sackville Rd., Bexhill-on-Sea, Sussex, England.